THE T-CLASS SUBMARINE

▼
A view of *Triton*
showing the very high
conning tower,
subsequently lowered in
all following submarines,
and the tall W/T mast.
(Wright and Logan)

THE T-CLASS SUBMARINE

THE CLASSIC BRITISH DESIGN
Paul J. Kemp

ARMS AND
ARMOUR

Acknowledgements

It gives me great pleasure to express my gratitude to the following who served in T-class submarines for their contributions to this book: Lieutenant-Commander A. F. Bagley; Commander John Bull; J. K. Chapman; Captain John Coote; George Cuddon; Charles Deleay; Lieutenant-Commander R. B. Foster; Captain Richard Gatehouse; Lieutenant-Commander Peter Hay; R. G. Jones; Commander W. D. A. King; Stan Law; Commander G. S. Mellor; L. S. Morrison; Commander Arthur Pitt; Reverend Ewan Pinsent; Commander R. G. Raikes; Vice-Admiral Sir John Roxburgh; Ron Slade; T. J. Soar; Captain J. S. Stevens; Vice-Admiral Sir Anthony Troup; A. Turville; Lieutenant-Commander Michael Wilson.

I am also deeply grateful to Lisa Adderley; Marija Batica; Ian Buxton; D. K. Brown, RCNC; J. D. Brown and the staff of Naval Historical Branch at the Ministry of Defence, particularly Lieutenant-Commander Arnold Hague, Bob Coppock and M. McAloon; Commander Richard Compton-Hall, Director of the Royal Navy Submarine Museum; Colin Bruce and Allison Duffield of the Department of Printed Books at the Imperial War Museum; Anne-Marie Ehrlich; L. L. von Munching; David Topliss and Bob Todd of the National Maritime Museum; National Portrait Gallery; the Historical Branch of the Royal Netherlands Navy; Dr. Achille Rastelli; David Webb and Wright & Logan of Portsmouth together with my colleagues in the Department of Photographs at the Imperial War Museum who have nobly endured my obsession with these submarines.

Special thanks are due to Vice-Admiral Sir Hugh Mackenzie for agreeing to write the foreword, Commander Reggie Fitzgerald for opening many doors for me, David Hill for his excellent line-drawings and for reading the manuscript, David Gibbons and Anthony Evans of DAG Publications, Frances Hutchinson for proofreading and editing the manuscript; and lastly but by no means least, Gus Britton of the Royal Navy Submarine Museum for his coffee and continual encouragement.

Any errors in what follows are exclusively my responsibility.

For Lisa, who was there at the beginning.

First published in Great Britain in 1990 by Arms and Armour Press, Villiers House, 41–47 Strand, London WC2N 5JE.

Distributed in Australia by Capricorn Link (Australia) Pty. Ltd, P.O. Box 665, Lane Cove, New South Wales 2066.

© Paul J. Kemp, 1990

British Library Cataloguing in Publication Data
Kemp, Paul
The T-class submarine.
1. Submarines
I. Title
623.8257
ISBN 0-85368-958-X

Jacket illustrations: front, HMS *Taku* at sea in the eastern Mediterranean in January 1943; painting by Geoff Shaw. Back, HMS *Thunderbolt*'s company with their 'Jolly Roger' on their return to the UK from the Mediterranean in March 1942.

Line illustrations by David Hill and Marija Batica.

Designed and edited by DAG Publications Ltd. Designed by David Gibbons; edited by Michael Boxall; layout by Anthony A. Evans; typeset by Typesetters (Birmingham) Ltd, Warley, West Midlands; camerawork by M&E Reproductions, North Fambridge, Essex; printed and bound in Great Britain by Courier International, Tiptree, Essex.

Contents

Foreword

by Vice-Admiral Sir Hugh Mackenzie, KCB, DSO*, DSC

I am honoured to write this foreword to the history of a class of submarine that achieved much in war and peace; and suffered also.

Conceived in the mid-1930s in a welter of conflicting demands – somewhat nebulous operational requirements playing second fiddle to limitations imposed by Naval Disarmament Treaties – the T-class submarine nevertheless evolved just in time to bear the full brunt of war and to take a (if not THE) major part in the very significant role played by British submarines during the Second World War, especially in Home Waters and in the Mediterranean. Many will consider they proved to be a highly successful design for these theatres: formidably armed, versatile, of adequate endurance, capable of withstanding heavy punishment and, by the standards of those days, providing good living conditions on board.

In the more distant waters of the Far East and Pacific limitations became more obvious: the lack of efficient air conditioning when dived and their comparatively low speed on the surface. This latter put them at a severe disadvantage where the wide open spaces of the Pacific and lack of long-range, anti-submarine Japanese air patrols permitted the tactics of surface operations and night surface attacks. In the light of this it seems ironic that the original Staff Requirement called for a submarine to fight a war against Japan, albeit from bases in Hong Kong and Singapore!

The value of the T class continued long after the war, but in another guise. With the role of the British submarine being directed primarily to anti-submarine warfare, those of the class that survived the immediate post-war scrapping programme proved to be an excellent test bed for new tactics to suit the new primary role and the control and use of higher underwater speeds: thus paving the way for the ultra silent and potentially highly successful anti-submarine submarines of the *Porpoise* and *Oberon* classes and setting the scene for the nuclear hunter-killer submarine.

Much of my 'submarine life' was spent in and with T-class submarines, and for me the 'T boat' will always remain something very special. Paul Kemp has brought much vividly back to life for me personally; but he has done far more, a very great deal more, than that. He has accomplished, in great detail, a unique history of a class of submarine that fully proved its worth in both war and peace, in many and varied roles. In covering their many aspects he has disclosed that each and every one of the 53 T-class submarines put into service has an individual story to tell, some more interesting, some more distinguished or, sadly, some more tragic than others; but all in all amounting to a very great wealth of facts. experience and knowledge. That he has so ably compressed it all into this unique and remarkable history is a triumph which deserves our attention and gratitude. It is entirely fitting that it should take its place in the archives of naval history, and that it also stands alongside those other memorials to all those who served in submarines, of whatever class or age.

Sylvan Lodge
Puttenham

Hugh Mackenzie
November 1989

▶
HMS *Triton*, first of the fifty-three T-class submarines, shows off her fine lines as she leaves Portsmouth in June 1939. (Wright and Logan)

1. The 1,000-ton Submarine

'It has been apparent to many Submarine and other Officers that the new construction submarines built and delivered since the war are not nearly as well thought out as they should have been.'[1]

Thus wrote Captain (E) George Villar in December 1934 when describing British submarine development since 1918 and, indeed, he had a point. During the First World War the Royal Navy amassed a vast amount of experience with submarines embodying every conceivable hull form and means of propulsion. The experience gained seems to have been completely ignored during the post-war period. British submarine development proceeded along two distinct lines: the Patrol and the Fleet Submarine. Patrol Submarines were intended for independent operations off the enemy coast against enemy warships and commerce. Fleet Submarines were considerably larger and designed with a high surface speed in order for them to operate with the main battle fleet. The first British post-war design for a patrol submarine was HMS *Oberon* (1,810/2,157 tons displacement, eight 21-inch torpedo tubes, one 4-inch gun) built in 1926. She set the pattern for a further eighteen submarines of the *Oxley*, O, P and R classes. They were all roughly similar in design and all had the same faults. They were large, slow, mechanically unreliable – *Oberon* acquired the dubious nickname of the 'Electro-Mechanical Monstrosity' – and over-complicated, and in the words of Captain Villar 'totally unsuited to the rigours of war'.[2]

The concept of the Fleet Submarine which had proved somewhat flawed in the First World War with the steam-driven K-class submarines enjoyed a new lease of life in the inter-war period. First there was the 'experimental' monster X.1 of 2,780/3,600 tons and armed with six 21-inch torpedo tubes and four 5.25-inch

guns. She was followed by the three *River*-class combined fleet and patrol submarines designed for a very high surface speed but which had a smaller armament than an *Oberon* (only six 21-inch torpedo tubes) on a hull nearly a third again as large.

The S-class coastal submarines of 730/927 tons and armed with six 21-inch torpedo tubes and a 3-inch gun marked a return to a more sensible design, but perpetuated many of the faults of the preceding classes. There seemed to be little liaison between submariners and the officials in the Director of Naval Construction's (DNC) department, and indeed where design was concerned, there was a certain hostility to any suggestions emanating from outside DNC. By the beginning of 1934 British submarine design was in a sorry state yet decisions had to be made on a replacement for the O, P and R classes which, under the terms of the Washington Treaty, would have to be retired after thirteen years' service. *Oberon* would, therefore, have to pay off in August 1940 with the others following thereafter.

A further consideration which pressed for a decision regarding future submarine construction was the approach of the 1935 London Naval Disarmament Conference which was sure to impose limits on submarine construction. The O, P and R classes had been designed for long-range operations in the Far East where, in the absence of a battlefleet, submarines were Britain's principal offensive weapon against the might of the Japanese Navy. Since the new submarines, at this stage existing under the designation 'Repeat P'

◀
HMS *Phoenix*, one of nineteen submarines of the O, P and R classes, built after the First World War, which proved less than satisfactory in service.

▼◀
Admiral Sir Noel Laurence who, as Rear-Admiral (Submarines), proposed an alternative double-hull design for a submarine to replace the O, P and R classes. (National Portrait Gallery)

▼
Sir Arthur Johns, Director of Naval Construction, who opposed Laurence's design and whose arguments carried the day. (D. K. Brown)

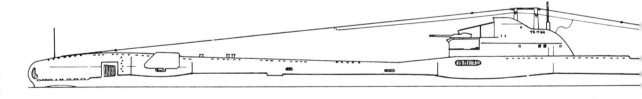

Triton as completed, showing the high conning tower with the open bridge.

class, would be replacing the O, P and R boats in this theatre, they had to be capable of the same endurance, but be appreciably smaller in view of possible future treaty restrictions, and easier to maintain.

The Admiralty considered the matter early in 1934. Under the terms of the 1930 London Naval Treaty Britain was restricted to a total submarine tonnage of 52,700 (standard surfaced displacement) and individual boats had to be below 2,000 tons with a maximum gun armament of one 5.1-inch. The forthcoming conference would undoubtedly demand a reduction in this amount: indeed in July 1932 the Americans had recommended an individual limit of 1,200 tons per boat which the Admiralty rejected on the grounds that it would exclude the *Porpoise*-class minelayers. The Admiralty was also concerned that too great a reduction in individual tonnage limits would result in a rash of small submarines being built by Britain's naval rivals which would be harder to find and sink than a smaller number of large submarines. Accordingly the Admiralty recommended sticking to the 2,000-ton limit in the hope that national pride would cause Britain's competitors to build up to the limit as they were already doing with cruisers.

At this point there was a divergence in thinking between the Admiralty and the Government over the future of the submarine. The Conservative government of Stanley Baldwin wanted to see the abolition of the submarine altogether, or at the very least an individual tonnage limit of 250 tons. The Admiralty was fairly certain that this proposal would be unacceptable and that some lesser limits of individual and total submarine tonnage would be agreed, so plans for the new submarine continued on the assumption that submarines would continue to be a part of Britain's naval forces for the foreseeable future.

In drawing up the requirements for the future submarine fleet the Admiralty estimated as follows: six minelayers (9,390 tons), twenty 'Replace P' type (20,000 tons), twelve S class (8,040 tons) and six 'Replace H' training submarines (2,400 tons) – the three *River*-class submarines do not seem to have figured in the Admiralty's future projections of the submarine fleet. This was a total of 44 units and a total tonnage of 39,830.

Accordingly the Admiralty's submission for the 1935 disarmament conference was to propose a quantative limit of 45 units and a total tonnage of 45,000.

The Admiralty's assessment of the likely outcome of the Second London Naval Disarmament Conference as regards submarines was fairly accurate. The Second London Naval Treaty was signed on 25 March 1936 between Britain, America and France; Japan having withdrawn from the international system of limiting naval armaments by treaty. The British Government's proposal for the complete abolition of the submarine or, failing that, a reduction to an individual limit of 250 tons was rejected. The individual tonnage limit for submarines of 2,000 tons and gun armament of a maximum calibre of 5.1-inch remained unaltered. In the absence of Japan, it proved impossible to agree any form of quantative limitation. To all intents and purposes, international regulation of naval armaments by treaty was over. The design for the 'Repeat Ps' was drawn up before the treaty was signed. Nevertheless, the prospect of treaty restrictions on submarine construction was an important factor throughout the design process.

Meanwhile on 27 February 1934 DNC had been asked to investigate designs for a patrol submarine of about 1,000 tons' displacement. However the DNC was not to enjoy a monopoly on submarine design because Rear-Admiral (Submarines), Rear-Admiral Noel Laurence, had very determined ideas of his own regarding the new submarines. Laurence was one of the most distinguished British submariners of the Great War. While in command of *E.1* in the Baltic he torpedoed and damaged the battlecruiser *Moltke* on 19 August 1915. Just over a year later on 5 November 1916, now in command of *J.1*, Laurence fired a four-torpedo salvo at a German battle squadron and succeeded in hitting *Grosser Kurfürst* and *Kronprinz Wilhelm* – the only occasion in submarine history when two capital ships have been hit in the same attack.

In the Far East the 'Repeat Ps' would find themselves facing the might of the Imperial Japanese Navy and, in the absence of other British naval forces, would find themselves pretty much on their own. An impressive torpedo armament was essential. Recent exercises had confirmed Laurence's opinion that it was becoming more and more difficult to penetrate a destroyer screen and therefore the submarine would have to shoot at a fast-moving target from a considerable distance. If necessary, the submarine would have to be able to fire on information supplied by ASDICs since periscope observation might not be possible. Laurence was convinced that a British submarine facing a fast, heavily escorted Japanese battle squadron needed a large torpedo armament to ensure a reasonable chance of a hit.

On 9 January 1934 Laurence had already proposed his own design based on the *River* class which was for a 2,115-ton boat built with a double hull rather than saddle tanks, which Laurence considered gave

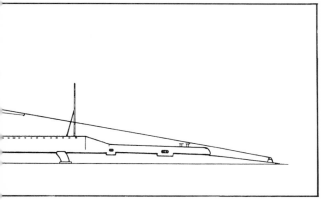

superior protection against depth-charge attack, and formidably armed with six internal bow tubes and the incredible number of twelve 'upper deck' or 'external' tubes mounted between the casing and the pressure hull.[3] The externals were arranged in four groups of three: two groups forward of the conning tower and two groups aft. The forward six faced diagonally outward to starboard, the after six tubes faced diagonally out to port. However, in the light of the Admiralty's meeting on 27 February 1934 which effectively spelt the end of the *River*-class programme, Laurence proposed a revised design on 16 April 1934 which was for a double-hulled boat of 1,086 tons standard displacement and armed with eight bow torpedo tubes with four external tubes arranged in two pairs forward and aft of the conning tower. Space precludes a more detailed discussion of this design but it is a most interesting one.

On 19 April, the DNC, Sir Arthur Johns, submitted two similar designs in response to the Admiralty's request. Labelled DNC 'A' and DNC 'B', they are compared with Laurence's and shown in the following table.

Table 1

	DNC 'A'	DNC 'B'	RA(S)
Length (oa)	260ft	250ft	256ft
Beam	22ft	22ft	21ft 6in
Mean surface draught in diving trim	15ft 6in	15ft 7in	18ft
Surface displacement	1,260 tons	1,195 tons	1,330 tons
Standard displacement	1,065 tons	990 tons	1,086 tons
Submerged displacement	1,540 tons	1,456 tons	1,664 tons
BHP of engines	2,500	2,500	3,050
Surface speed	14.8kts	15kts	16.5kts
Endurance			
at 8kts	9,500nm	11,000nm	N/A
at 11kts	6,000nm	7,200nm	10,000nm
Oil fuel	99 tons	109 tons	162 tons
Number of battery cells	336	224	N/A
Number of motors	2	2	N/A
HP of motors	1,300	1,300	1,300
Submerged speed	9kts	9kts	9kts
Submerged endurance			
at 9kts	2½hrs	1hr	2hrs
at 1½kts	80hrs	55hrs	85hrs
Torpedo tubes:			
internal	6	6	8
external	4	4	8
Reloads carried	6	6	8
Gun armament	one 3in	one 3in	one 4in
Diving depth	300ft	300ft	300ft
Complement	50	48	N/A[4]

Johns' and Laurence's designs are remarkably similar to one another, showing that Johns had adopted perhaps some of the features (notably the external torpedo tubes) listed in Laurence's submission of 9 January. Johns, however, proposed to mount the externals facing forward, one above the other on each side of the conning tower.[5] The most radical difference in the designs proposed by Johns and Laurence was in hull form. Johns stuck with the tried and tested single hull with saddle tanks while Laurence advocated the adoption of a double hull with the ballast tanks being

flooded through a duct keel form on the grounds that it would give greater protection when the boat was under depth-charge attack.

Johns replied to Laurence's suggestions on 22 June 1934[6] in a letter which dismissed the double-hull concept completely, arguing that the extra weight required for this method of construction (weight being a critical factor in the light of treaty restrictions) would be better employed in strengthening a single-hull structure which was already tried and tested. Johns was already familiar with the relative arguments for and against the double-hull form, having been involved in the controversy over the E- and G-class submarine comparison during the First World War: the E class being single-hull and the G class double-hull boats. The submariners pressed for the adoption of the double-hull type and once given it, in the form of the G class, didn't like it. The arguments against double hull are fairly complex, but briefly, a double-hull boat, having a bigger mass when dived, requires more power and has a higher centre of gravity than a single-hull boat.

With less than six months to go before being relieved as RA(S), Laurence could have little hope that his proposals would be adopted. In any case with the DNC so resolutely opposed to the double-hull concept there was little the Admiralty could do without provoking a first-class row. So the double-hull design with multiple external torpedo tubes died a death since Laurence's successor, Rear-Admiral C. P. Talbot, was not inclined to push the idea. Laurence, however, did not go without a last protest. On 7 December 1934, five days before he hauled down his flag, Laurence authorized Captain George Villar, an engineering officer on his staff, to release the correspondence between himself and DNC together with the supporting documentation and a very critical, but constructively argued, paper on British submarine design.[7] The Admiralty was furious: Laurence escaped their wrath, but the episode cost Villar his career. Ten years later both Laurence and Villar would have given wry smiles when the double-hull form was adopted for the A-class submarine.

Meanwhile the two DNC designs were going the rounds of the various Admiralty departments and formed the basis for the preliminary staff requirement which was drawn up in November 1934. It called for a submarine of 1,000-tons standard displacement armed with six internal 21in torpedo tubes and two external tubes, and one 4in or 3in gun (4in if stability permitted), and capable of 4,000 nautical miles at 11 knots plus sufficient fuel for a 28-day patrol which required 200 tons of fuel (including 30 per cent for foul bottom) which corresponded to 5,500nm at 11 knots. Submerged endurance was to be 15 hours at 2 knots and eight hours at 5 knots and a top submerged speed of 9 knots. Diving depth was to be 300 feet.

RA(S) concurred generally with these proposals, but would be content with a surface endurance of 3,000nm at 11 knots plus sufficient fuel for a 16½-day patrol with only a 10 per cent margin for a foul bottom. This was a figure equivalent to 4,500nm at 11 knots which was eventually accepted.

Early in 1935 Johns produced Design 'C' (see table 2) which embodied most of the staff requirements. The main alteration from 'A' and 'B' was the reduction in standard displacement to 1,000 tons to comply with treaty restrictions. It was impossible to compromise by accepting a smaller battery to save weight as in Design 'B' since this would limit underwater endurance. This would be unacceptable since the submarines would have to operate in northern latitudes, both in Home Waters and the Far East, where nights in summer are short, and the submarine would have to remain dived for most of the long day and would not have a lot of time to get a good charge in at night. Consequently a reduction in machinery space was ordered which meant a drop of speed to 14.5 knots and a reduction of surface endurance to 8,600nm at 8 knots had to be accepted.

Design 'C' was but an interim measure before the submission of the preliminary legend, or Design 'D' (see table 2) on 23 April 1935. Johns admitted that the displacement had risen to 1,075 tons because of the need to store all the oil fuel within the pressure hull: stowage of fuel in external tanks, which was standard in O-, P- and R-class submarines, was no longer considered acceptable. Johns pointed out that to obtain a standard displacement of 1,000 tons the length would have to be decreased by 13 feet and endurance reduced to 2,400nm at 11 knots. This was unacceptable to Talbot,

since such a reduction would gravely reduce the boat's ability to conduct an extended patrol in the Far East, so standard displacement had to rise to 1,075 tons.

Another alteration was in the layout of the external torpedo tubes. Johns now proposed that they be arranged in two forward-facing pairs: the first to be fitted under the bow casing above the six internal forward tubes and the second placed one on each side of the bridge.

At a meeting on 1 May 1935[8] called by the Controller, and attended by Rear-Admiral (Submarines), Assistant Chief of the Naval Staff, Director of Naval Construction, Deputy Engineer in Chief, Director of Naval Equipment and Director of Electrical Equipment, the design was broadly agreed with the important exception that the length should be shortened by 30 feet to bring the displacement below 1,000, if necessary accommodating some fuel in pressure-tight exterior tanks. After DNC had considered the matter he reported that a 30-foot reduction in length would require major redesign work and it was approved to reduce the length by merely 15 feet. It was also agreed to reduce the fresh water diving requirement from those with a specific gravity of 1010 to those of 1020 (in other words, water with a higher salt content), which enabled 13 tons of fuel to be carried allowing another 500nm at 11 knots. However, it was accepted that should the boat be required to operate in the Black Sea or the Baltic – shades of the Great War – where the water is almost completely fresh, she would have to sail some 26 tons short of fuel, but in view of

▶
The ill-fated *Thetis* goes down the ways at Cammell Laird's Birkenhead shipyard on 29 June 1938.

the limited area of operations in these theatres this was not considered too great a disadvantage. The design as agreed is shown in the following table.

Table 2

	Design 'C'	Design 'D'	Final Design
Length (oa)	250ft	291ft 6in	276ft 6in
Beam	22ft	24ft 3in	25ft 6in
Mean surface draught in diving trim	15ft 7in	13ft 6in	12ft 9in fwd 14ft 7in aft
Surface displacement	1,195 tons	1,290 tons	1,290 tons
Standard displacement	1,000 tons	1,075 tons	1,090 tons
Submerged displacement	1,455 tons	1,560 tons	1,560 tons
BHP of engines	2,300	2,500	2,500
Surface speed	14½kts	15½kts	15½kts
Endurance			
at 8kts	8,600nm	N/A	N/A
at 11kts	5,500nm	4,500nm	4,500nm
Oil fuel	87 tons	135 tons	135 tons
Number of battery cells	336	336	336
Number of motors	4	4	4
HP of motors	1,300	1,450	1,450
Submerged speed	9kts	9kts	9kts
Submerged endurance			
at 9kts	2½hrs	1½hrs	
at 1½kts	80hrs	55hrs (at 2½kts)	
Torpedo tubes:			
internal	6	6	6
external	4	4	4
Reloads carried	6	6	6
Gun armament	one 3in	one 4in	one 4in
Diving depth	300ft	300ft	300ft
Complement	50	44	48[9]

Table of Weights for Design D

Item	Weight (tons)
General equipment:	25
HP compressor and air bottles:	12
Armament	
torpedo:	65
gun:	8
Machinery:	115
CO_2 Plant:	3
Main battery:	145
Main motors:	40
Fuel oil:	135
Lubricating oil:	15
Trimming, compensating and fresh water:	65
Hull and ballast keel:	660
Total:	1,290

Following the 1 May meeting the formal staff requirement was drawn up. The design acquired a formal name when on 24 June 1935 the anonymous 'Repeat P' designation was dropped and the Admiralty decided that all boats of the class should bear names beginning with the letter 'T'. On 3 September 1935 *Triton* was selected as the name for the first of the class.[10]

Matters now proceeded apace. Tenders were invited from Vickers, Cammell Laird and Scotts on 5 December 1935 and the design received the final approval of the Admiralty Board on 13 February 1936. On 5 March 1936 *Triton* was ordered from Vickers Armstrong at Barrow under the 1935 Programme. Launched on 5 October

British Inter-war Submarine Designs

	Odin (O Class)	Clyde (River Class)	Triton
Displacement:	1,475 tons	1,850 tons	1,090 tons
Length (oa):	283ft 6in	345ft	276ft 6in
Beam:	29ft 11in	28ft 3in	25ft 6in
Mean surface draught in diving trim:	16ft 1in	15ft 11in	12ft 9in fwd
Machinery:	2 shaft diesels, + electric motors, 4,520bhp/ 1,390shp = 17.5/8 knots.	2 shaft super-charged diesels + electric motors, 10,000bhp/ 2,500shp = 22/10 knots.	2 shaft diesels + electric motors 2,500bhp/14 50shp = 15½/ 9 knots.
Armament:	8 × 21in torpedo tubes (6 bow, 2 stern), 1 × 4in gun.	6 × torpedo tubes (all bow), 1 × 4in gun.	10 × 21in torpedo tubes (all forward firing), 1 × 4in gun.
Complement:	53	61	48

1937, she ran her first of class trials in December 1938 and, indeed, because of the outbreak of war in September 1939, was the only boat to conduct a full series of trials. Her commanding officer, Lieutenant-Commander H. P. de C. Steele, reported that 'the ship handles very well under all surface conditions . . . submerged handling was also good, but depth-keeping at 30ft required much practice.'[11]

The cost of *Triton* was £299,084 while *Triumph*, the next to complete, cost £305,038. The average cost of a wartime-built T-boat was slightly over £400,000,[12] the increase being due more to wartime inflation rather than any signficant increase in cost.

The building programme as envisaged before the outbreak of war was as follows.

1935 Programme Vickers Armstrong: *Triton*
1936 Programme Cammell Laird: *Thetis*, *Trident*; Vickers Armstrong: *Triumph*; Scotts: *Tribune*
1937 Programme Cammell Laird: *Taku*; Vickers Armstrong: *Thistle*, *Tarpon*, *Triad*, *Truant*; Scotts: *Tuna*; Chatham Dockyard: *Tigris*
1938 Programme Vickers Armstrong: *Tetrarch*; Chatham Dockyard: *Torbay*; Cammell Laird: *Talisman*

The three boats of the 1938 Programme are of some interest as they were configured as minelayers carrying mines in vertical wells in the saddle tanks (see Chapter 4 for discussion of the system). On 16 March 1939 the Admiralty had asked Vickers to quote for installing a minelaying system based on that fitted to the two Vickers-built Estonian submarines *Kalev* and *Lembit*. Only *Tetrarch* was completed in this configuration and as such her surface displacement was 1,365 tons and she carried 3 tons less fuel oil with a consequent reduction in endurance.[13]

It was planned to order five boats under the 1939 Programme together with another five each year under

▲
HMS *Truant*, launched at
Vickers' Barrow yard on 5
May 1939. In contrast to
Thetis, her periscope
standards are erected, but
she has not yet been fitted
with her 4-inch gun.

▶
Job No. 1027, ex-HMS
Thetis, in Cammell Laird's
dry dock after being raised
following her loss during
her first dive on 1 June
1939. She was extensively
refitted by Cammell Laird
before recommissioning
as *Thunderbolt*.

◀

Mrs Barry (centre), wife of Rear-Admiral (Submarines), Rear-Admiral Claude Barry (left), prepares to send *Telemachus* down the ways at Barrow on 19 June 1943. Sir James Callender (right), General Manager of Vickers' Barrow works, watches pensively. (IWM A.17453)

▶

Moments later *Telemachus* is afloat and ready for the tow to the fitting out jetty. (IWM A.17454)

▶▶

HRH Prince Bernhard of the Netherlands takes the salute as *Zwaardvis* commissions at Barrow on 6 December 1943. The censor has done his best to remove the pennant number and the 291W radar aerial. The submarine's name is spelt *Zwaardfisch*, a spelling which was altered after the Second World War to the less Germanic *Zwaardvis*. (Royal Netherlands Navy)

the 1940 and 1941 Programmes, with four boats under the 1942 Programme, bringing the total to 34 units. The outbreak of the Second World War on 3 September 1939 naturally meant an expansion in the building programme. The urgent need was for numbers of submarines and it was imperative that construction should not be held up by the delays usually associated with a new design. However, submarine construction is a specialized business and there were only three commercial yards: Vickers, Cammell Laird and Scotts together with the Royal Dockyard at Chatham that had recent experience in this field. The 1939 Programme was increased to seven boats, but this was the maximum that could be handled by the industry. A further five T-class minelayers like *Tetrarch* were ordered on 9 October 1939: two from Scotts and three from Cammell Laird. The order was confirmed on 2 January 1940, but abruptly cancelled on 29 January 1940 to be replaced by five S-class submarines, early operations in the North Sea having shown that the S boats were more suitable for these shallower waters.

Vickers were the main contractor for the T-class submarines, building 29 of the 53 boats. The involvement of the other two commercial yards was reduced since Cammell Laird gave up their T-class contracts in order to concentrate on building S-class submarines. Likewise Scotts built four of the early boats, with *Tabard* transferred from Vickers, but Scotts' yard suffered heavily at the hands of the Luftwaffe, and *Trooper*,

then existing under the undignified title of Job No. 1108, was knocked off the blocks during an air raid on the night of 6/7 May 1941. The damage set back her completion by some three months compared to *Traveller* being built in the same yard. The air-raid damage caused the yard virtually to give up submarine production throughout the critical period of the war.

Although Vickers remained the lead yard, the war saw a growing involvement on the part of the Royal Dockyards. By the end of the T-class construction programme Portsmouth, Chatham and Devonport Dockyards were building more T boats than Vickers. Chatham Dockyard, in particular, was considerably experienced at submarine building and had already built *Tigris* of the 1937 Programme and *Torbay* of the 1938 Programme. The reason for this change was that Vickers could not produce as many T boats as they hoped or as the Admiralty required. At the beginning of the war Vickers had claimed to be able to build sixteen T class a year. By January 1942 this estimate had been reduced to eight boats a year. In early 1941 Admiral (Submarines), Admiral Sir Max Horton, became seriously concerned at the length of time it was taking to complete *Trusty* and *Turbulent*, the two boats of the 1939 Programme allocated to Vickers. His concern was motivated not only by the fact that the boats were desperately needed at sea, but that orders had been placed with Vickers for all nine boats of the 1940

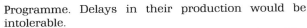

Programme. Delays in their production would be intolerable.

The problems at Vickers were many and various. The yard was suffering from the attentions of the Luftwaffe, but, as Horton pointed out, so was Cammell Laird whose production of S-class submarines was on schedule. Over-optimism by Vickers' staff as to how soon work could be completed was another factor, as was the bad influence of some 'Red' apprentices, but the root cause was that Vickers was over-extended with T- and U-class submarine construction, merchant ship construction and warship refits. Horton could do little more than cajole and plead in his own inimitable way for the submarines to be given priority, for non-essential work to be diverted away from Vickers, and for the yard to have priority in the allocation of labour.

But the situation was not solely Vickers' fault. There was a certain amount of confusion at the Admiralty regarding the procurement of submarines. Reference had already been made to the sudden ordering and equally abrupt cancellation of five T class from Cammell Laird and Scotts in 1940. In 1941 a similar situation occurred when on 6 June four Ts were ordered from Vickers' yard at High Walker on the Tyne – which had never yet constructed a T boat – but were cancelled on 30 June to be replaced by V class. This haphazard method of ordering submarines without regard to output undoubtedly caused disruption in the shipyards. Horton could not have his cake and eat it. A more permanent solution was greater use of the Royal Dockyards.

As a result of Horton's concern about Vickers' ability to deliver, six of the sixteen boats in the 1941 Programme went to the Royal Dockyards: two each to Chatham, Portsmouth and Devonport. In fact Horton's fears for the boats of the 1940 Programme were groundless; their average completion time was one year and three months: *Tantalus*, built in 11¾ months, took the least time of any of the Vickers-built boats in peace or war. However, for the ten Vickers-built boats of the 1941 Programme the completion time had increased to an average of seventeen months, but this was undoubtedly due to the extra equipment and modifications dictated as a result of war experience.

The boats allocated to the Royal Dockyards undoubtedly took some of the pressure off Vickers, but the move could hardly be regarded as a success, for it did not result in the submarines being completed any quicker. Chatham's pair under the 1941 Programme, *Trenchant* and *Tradewind*, took an average of twenty months to complete – against seventeen months for a Vickers boat – and the two given to Devonport, *Thule* and *Tudor*, took an average of 29 months. But *Tireless*, allocated along with *Token* to Portsmouth, took an epic 41¼ months to build. It was often sarcastically noted that the only action that *Tireless* saw was when a concrete mixer fell off the dockyard wall and onto her casing.[14] Portsmouth and Devonport had not built submarines for many years and it took time to develop the necessary skills. All three dockyards suffered more than commercial yards in continually having their labour force diverted to other work to the detriment of the submarine programme. Portsmouth Dockyard in particular was heavily committed to work connected with the Normandy invasion, and their submarine jobs tended to take longer than anywhere else. On completion of work-up and her first patrol, *Tantalus* (Lieutenant-Commander H. S. Mackenzie) was taken in hand by Portsmouth Dockyard to have the riveted seams of her external ballast tanks welded-up since Nos. 3 and 5 were being used as fuel tanks, before she deployed to the Far East. Her commanding officer, now Vice-Admiral Sir Hugh Mackenzie, recalled that '. . . Vickers reckoned they could do the job in a week but their Lordships decided otherwise and after work-up we must go to Portsmouth Dockyard and have our ballast tanks converted which took nearly three months. We were bottom priority, the dockyard were working flat out building Mulberry Harbours and so having worked-up and done our working-up patrol we were back in the dockyard – it was soul-destroying'.[15]

In the 1942 Programme the balance between Vickers and the Royal Dockyards was reversed with the Dockyards building six of the ten boats while two of the four allocated to Vickers were transferred to Scotts as is shown in the following table.

1939 Programme Vickers Armstrong: *Trusty, Truculent*; Cammell Laird: *Thrasher, Thorn, Tempest*; Scotts: *Traveller, Trooper*
1940 Programme Vickers Armstrong: P.311 (The only boat not to receive a name: she was lost on operations in January 1943 before the name *Tutankhamen* could be formally allocated), *Trespasser, Taurus, Tactician, Truculent, Templar, Tally-Ho, Tantalus, Tantivy*
1941 Programme Chatham Dockyard: *Tradewind, Trenchant*; Devonport Dockyard: *Thule, Tudor*; Portsmouth Dockyard:

Tireless, Token; Vickers Armstrong: *Telemachus, Zwaardvis* (ex-*Talent*), *Terrapin, Thorough, Tiptoe, Trump, Taciturn, Tapir, Tijgerhaai* (ex-*Tarn*), *Teredo, Talent* (ex-*Tasman*).
1942 Programme Devonport Dockyard: *Totem, Truncheon*; Chatham Dockyard: *Turpin, Thermopylae*; Vickers Armstrong: *Theban*, Threat**; Portsmouth Dockyard: *Thor*, Tiara**; Scotts: *Tabard, Talent**. * = Cancelled. A further four boats, numbered P.345 to P.348, were projected, and the name *Typhoon* proposed for one of them, but never ordered, being cancelled in favour of A-class submarines.

Two of the 1941 Programme boats allocated to Vickers were transferred to the Royal Netherlands Navy: *Talent* was renamed *Zwaardvis* (Swordfish) and *Tarn* became *Tijgerhaai* (Tigershark). Both boats took slightly longer than the average to complete because of alterations to bring them into line with Dutch practice. The Dutch were the only one of Britain's allies to receive a T-class submarine, the Greeks, Poles, Norwegians and Free French having to make do with the smaller U-class boats. The Dutch had a greater number of qualified submarine personnel than the other Allied navies and so were better able to man a T-class boat, but the transfer was also in recognition of the superb fighting record of the Dutch submarine fleet which had come over to Britain *en masse* in 1940. *Tijgerhaai* completed too late to see any war service, but *Zwaardvis*, under the command of the intrepid Lieutenant-Commander H. A. W. Goossens, had a distinguished war record.[16]

No further T boats were ordered after the 1942 Programme because the A-class design was well advanced. By May 1945 the T-boat construction programme was nearly complete with only nine boats still in builders' hands. Of these *Token* (Portsmouth DY), *Tabard* (Scotts), *Thermopylae* (Chatham DY) and *Teredo* (Vickers) were completed, while *Thor, Tiara* (Portsmouth DY), *Theban, Threat* (Vickers) and *Talent* [ii] (Scotts) were cancelled on 29 October 1945.

◄
Tasman makes a fine sight as she goes down the ways at Barrow on 13 February 1945. Note the bulge of the saddle tanks on the starboard side of the pressure hull. *Tasman* was renamed *Talent* in April 1945 since the original *Talent* had become the Dutch *Zwaardvis*. (IWM A.27386)

Token (centre) and *Tireless* (inboard) fitting out in Portsmouth Dockyard on 25 May 1944. In both submarines the two midships external tubes have not yet been fitted, but in both cases No. 11 tube at the stern can be clearly seen. The outboard submarine is the French *Orione*. (National Maritime Museum)

▼
Thor and *Tiara* lying alongside the repair ship *Ranpura* at Portsmouth Dockyard in the summer of 1944. Although launched, they are in a very early stage of fitting out. The casing is complete only over the bows and the outboard boat has no plating over her saddle tanks, the frames for which can be clearly seen. Both boats were later scrapped while under construction. (National Maritime Museum)

2. Hull, Superstructure and Propulsion

In the opinion of many, the T class were the most graceful-looking submarines ever designed and built for the Royal Navy. From the big bulbous bow containing the two external torpedo tubes the casing sloped down towards the conning tower, where it rose again to accommodate the two midships external tubes before running down to a slim stern. In terms of external appearance the Ts can be divided into three groups:

Group One *Triton, Thetis, Triumph, Trident, Tribune, Thistle, Taku, Tarpon, Triad, Truant, Tuna, Tigris, Tetrarch, Talisman* and *Torbay*
Group Two *Thrasher, Thorn, Trusty, Turbulent, Tempest, Traveller* and *Trooper*
Group Three *P.311, Trespasser, Taurus, Tactician, Truculent, Templar, Tally-Ho, Tantalus, Tradewind, Trenchant, Thule, Tudor, Tireless, Token, Telemachus, Zwaardvis, Terrapin, Thorough, Tiptoe, Trump, Taciturn, Tapir, Tijgerhaai, Talent, Totem, Truncheon, Turpin, Thermopylae, Teredo* and *Tabard*

There were also important differences in appearance within each group. Of the Group One boats, *Triton, Thetis, Triumph, Trident* and *Tribune* had very bluff bows as a result of the bow caps for the bow external tubes being hinged horizontally. In the remainder of the Group One boats the bow caps were hinged vertically which gave a finer line to the bow with a smoother sweep of the bow into the hull shape proper and a smaller volume of floodable casing forward.[1] Even so the bows retained a fairly bluff form which, during the early part of the war, rapidly became the source of complaints that its shape affected speed when on the surface. In January 1940 *Trident* (Lieutenant-Commander A. G. L. Seale) reported that in the slightest lop, the bows caused a loss of one knot, in seas of state 1–2 a loss of 2 knots and in sea state 3–4 before the beam a loss of 4 knots or more.[2] As a result of these complaints the Admiralty decided to omit the bow external tubes from two Ts: *Triumph* which was being repaired

following mine damage and *Thetis* which was being refitted after her tragic loss as a result of an accident in June 1939 before recommissioning as *Thunderbolt*. Accordingly both these boats completed without their bow external tubes which resulted in their having a much finer shape to their bows.[3] It is impossible to determine whether the finer bows in *Triumph* and *Thunderbolt* radically affected performance, as they both went to the Mediterranean on completing their refits where the weather conditions encountered were very different from those in home waters.

The height and shape of the bridge also differed in the Group One boats. *Triton* completed with a very high open bridge. During her first of class trials her commanding officer reported that the bridge was extremely draughty particularly in a direct head wind.[4] *Triton* was built with the fore end of the bridge 11 feet and the after end 8 feet 6 inches above the datum line (waterline with the submarine in standard displacement). In *Tribune* and later vessels the forward end was reduced to 10 feet and the after end raised to 9 feet 6 inches. However, this reduction did little to improve conditions; *Truant* (Lieutenant-Commander C. H. Hutchinson) reported in December 1939 that: 'The bridge was found to be very exposed during the heavy weather experienced today, 12 December 1939. The constant shipping of heavy seas greatly impaired the efficiency of OOWs and lookouts. Speed was reduced to avoid injury to personnel on the bridge.'[5]

The apparent solution lay in the fitting *Thunderbolt, Triumph* and *Tuna*, with a 'cab' bridge, a hook-like structure over the front of the bridge, which provided a degree of shelter for those on watch. *Tarpon* had a most unusual arrangement, being competed with a 'high' bridge similar to *Triton* which was then topped by a 'cab'. Although *Tarpon* had the briefest life of any T boat, DNC noted in his post-war analysis that the arrangement was 'not satisfactory'.[6] Of the other

HMS *Tuna*: a Group One boat showing wartime modifications including the fitting of a 20mm Oerlikon gun and 291W radar. Note that *Tuna* has retained her cab bridge. The aerial at the forward end of the periscope standards is for the experimental trials with 267 combined air and surface warning radar.

HMS *Tribune* goes slowly astern away from an S-class submarine moored alongside the depot ship *Maidstone* as she leaves Algiers for patrol in February 1943. Note the bluff shape of the bows, common to *Triton*, *Thetis*, *Triumph* and *Trident*, and the shape of the orifices for the two external bow tubes. (IWM A.14459)

Group One boats, *Tetrarch*, *Torbay* and *Talisman* were likewise fitted with a 'cab'. *Torbay*, however, reverted to having an open bridge before going to the Far East.

The Group One boats received the greatest number of alterations as a result of war experience. These included the fitting of Type 291W radar on a mast at the after end of the periscope standards, a 20mm Oerlikon in a bandstand mounting at the after end of the conning tower in *Thunderbolt*, *Trident*, *Taku*, *Truant*, *Tuna*, *Tigris*, *Talisman* and *Torbay*, and an additional stem torpedo tube.

The one aspect of the Ts' torpedo armament that was unsatisfactory was the lack of a stern salvo: all ten tubes faced forward. There had been considerable debate about the introduction of stern tubes in British submarines. Objectors claimed that two tubes, all that could be fitted into the stern, were quite ineffective when fired on a fixed bearing. Moreover the space taken up by stern tubes was urgently required for stores and accommodation and their omission would ease the burden of work on an already overburdened torpedo department. These arguments were swiftly overturned on the outbreak of war when several

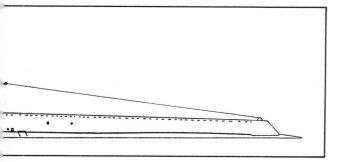

commanders complained about the lack of a stern salvo; *Triad* (Lieutenant-Commander E. F. Pizey) wistfully noted that the lack of a stern salvo was 'keenly felt' when two German destroyers passed astern in the path of the moon in April 1940.[7] In March 1942 *Torbay* (Commander A. C. C. Miers) was on the receiving end of a severe depth-charge attack which resulted from the submarine being detected while on the surface while Miers was turning to bring his bow tubes to bear. Miers complained that he would not have been detected had his submarine had a stern salvo.[8] The additional tube, known as No. 11, was fitted facing aft under the casing on the centre line. Of the Group One boats, *Taku*, *Thunderbolt*, *Tigris*, *Torbay*, *Tribune*, *Trident*, *Truant* and *Tuna* were fitted with this eleventh torpedo tube.

The seven Group Two boats presented a remarkably homogeneous appearance and in many ways had the most pleasing appearance of all the boats in the class. Gus Britton, a signalman in *Tribune*, remembers *Trooper*'s (Lieutenant J. S. Wraith) arrival at Algiers in March 1943: '. . . her elegant appearance. She was looking so good in her dark-blue Mediterranean livery with a new white ensign and her "Jolly Roger" flying.'[9]

All Group Two boats had their bows fined by placing the bow external tubes 7 feet further aft in an attempt to eliminate the problems of loss of speed which had dogged the earlier boats. The modification was successful, but resulted in the openings for 7 and 8 tubes being more pronounced. All boats were fitted with a cab-type bridge, but the most obvious modification was the repositioning of 9 and 10 tubes. They were moved aft of the conning tower and reversed so that they faced astern. No. 11 tube was also fitted as standard in all the Group Two boats. With eight forward-facing and

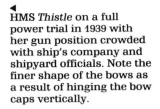

HMS *Thistle* on a full
power trial in 1939 with
her gun position crowded
with ship's company and
shipyard officials. Note the
finer shape of the bows as
a result of hinging the bow
caps vertically.

HMS *Thunderbolt* (ex-
Thetis) manoeuvring in
Holy Loch in January 1941
after her return from the
Bay of Biscay where she
had sunk the Italian
submarine *Tarantini* on 15
December 1940. The much
finer shape to the bows as
a result of removing the
bow external tubes is very
evident. (IWM A.2577)

HMS *Triumph* at sea in
May 1939 with both
periscopes raised and the
torpedo loading derrick
stowed on the casing aft of
the conning tower. The
photograph shows off the
lines of the casing of a
Group One T-class
submarine. Note also the
open bridge. (IWM HU.50)

three aft-facing tubes, the Group Twos had a more balanced arrangement of their torpedo armament. In *Thrasher, Thorn, Trusty, Turbulent* and *Tempest* the tubes were angled 10° off the centre line in order that the torpedoes would not foul the saddle tanks on being fired. However, this modification resulted in an unusually large area of flat casing which affected depth-keeping. In *Trooper* and *Traveller* this problem was solved by pulling in the tubes to an angle of 7° off the centre line.[10]

All the Group Two boats went to the Mediterranean from where only *Thrasher* and *Trusty* returned. Extensively refitted, including the addition of 291W radar and a 20mm Oerlikon, they lost their 'cab' bridges in favour of the open bridge.

The remaining boats form the third and final group of T boats. They represent the final development of the original design, but their construction reflected wartime priorities and austerity. Much inessential equipment such as ensign and jackstaffs, guardrails, stanchions and flag lockers was no longer fitted. One of the two anchors was also omitted and there were numerous modifications such as the Main Line, the submarine's internal pumping system for flooding

internal tanks, being made of steel rather than copper piping, and direct telemotor control of hydroplanes.

The shape of the bow was further fined so that the external tubes were contained in an undignified hump which did nothing for their looks however beneficial it proved in improving seakeeping. *P.311* and *Trespasser* were the only ones completed without an Oerlikon which was fitted as standard in the others. The casing around the conning tower and over 9 and 10 tubes was flattened down, reducing the 'hump' which had characterized the Group Two boats. The Group Three boats also reverted to having an open bridge. The cabs fitted to some Group One and all the Group Two boats were really a relic of peacetime when a boat could expect to spend some time on the surface and watchkeepers needed protection from the elements. In wartime the open bridge gave better all-round vision – a more important quality than questions of habitability. In any case all the Group Three boats were destined for the Far East where the bad weather found in Home Waters did not exist.

But the biggest change in the construction of the Group Three boats was the introduction of welding. The Royal Navy was reluctant to adopt welding for the

construction of warships in general and submarines in
particular. Pre-war trials against 'Job 81', a dumb target
vessel of both riveted and welded construction, proved
inconclusive and the experiment was not continued
after the outbreak of war. In May 1942 DNC was not
convinced of the virtues of welded construction: 'I do
not think that it can be concluded that a welded
pressure hull is superior to a riveted pressure hull.'[11]
Concern was also expressed about the quality of
workmanship involved in welded construction: 'With
welding the human element is much more critical than
with riveting. A welder producing inferior work would
prejudice the standard of production of the whole
submarine. It is not at all easy to devise tests which
will ensure that the requisite standard of work is
everywhere being obtained . . . It has also to be borne
in mind that to enable the pressure hull to be welded
at Vickers, say, the firm would have to train a greatly
increased number of welders who would have to collect
their practical experience on work of the highest
national importance.'[12]

Despite reservations on the part of DNC, the ship-
builders reacted very favourably to the proposal since
it would ease the workload on their riveting and

caulking departments. But the introduction of welding
was a slow process. Although welded T-bar framing
had been introduced for the three boats of the 1938
Programme and subsequent submarines, it was not
until July 1942 that the Admiralty sanctioned the use of
welding for the seams and butts of the pressure hull
and this decision was later extended to cover complete
construction of the submarine. The following boats
were of partly welded construction: *P.311, Trespasser,
Taurus, Tactician, Truculent, Templar, Tally-Ho, Tantalus,
Tradewind, Trenchant, Thule, Tudor, Zwaardvis, Terrapin*
and *Thorough*, while *Tiptoe, Trump, Taciturn, Tapir,
Tijgerhaai, Talent, Teredo, Tabard, Totem, Truncheon,
Turpin,* and *Thermopylae* were of completely welded
construction.

Welded construction conferred many advantages. 'S'
quality steel of 30lb replaced HST quality steel of 25lb
which made the hull far stronger: diving depth was
extended to 350 feet and *Tiptoe*, the first all-welded boat
to complete, was satisfactorily test-dived to 400 feet.
More importantly fuel could be carried in the external
ballast tanks thus increasing endurance. Since all the
Group Three boats were destined for the Far East
where the distances to and from patrol areas were

enormous this was of critical importance. Nos 3 and 5 ballast tanks were selected for this purpose, thus increasing oil fuel stowage from 135 tons to 215 tons which increased endurance to 11,000 nautical miles. The extra fuel reduced the reserve of buoyancy from 20 to 11 per cent, but only one boat, *Tudor*, reported any stability problems.[13]

The partly welded boats retained riveted construction for their external fuel tanks, but before proceeding to the Far East were taken in hand to have the tanks welded up so as to leave no tell-tale oil leaks. However, in order to prevent small leaks due to the working of the structure, or from punctures caused by small-arms fire, a sub-pressure pump installation was fitted. This enabled a small suction pressure of up to 2psi below sea pressure, to be brought on a leaking tank, which was quite effective in preventing leaks from cracks as wide as ⅓-inch and 8 to 12 inches long.[14]

Quality control of the welding was done by radiographic inspection, but other methods were also employed. Welds in HMS *Turpin* at Chatham Dockyard were tested by an internal air pressure of 150psi; certain hull valves had to be gagged as the pressure applied was in the reverse direction to that for which they had been designed.[15]

Irrespective of what group they came from, T boats proved easy to handle and possessed good diving and submerged control qualities. Commander R. P. Raikes who served in *Talisman* and commanded *Tribune* and *Tuna* remembered that their handling qualities . . . 'were remarkable in the T class. Handling on the surface in good weather, they were perfect. Both ahead and astern they turned quickly, they answered the helm quickly, they were remarkably manoeuvrable although they rolled like awful cows . . . *Tribune* was a joy to handle. They were very uncomfortable diving in heavy weather until you got down, then they were steady as a rock. *Talisman* was a dream to trim . . . you could catch a stopped trim quite easily.'[16]

The hulls of T boats proved remarkably strong. Their depth limit was 300 feet, for a riveted boat, yet *Triumph*, *Truant*, *Trident*, *Talisman*, *Tigris*, *Tribune* and *Templar* all

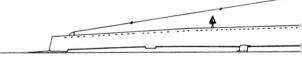

HMS *Thunderbolt* (ex-*Thetis*) in late 1942 on completion of her second wartime refit. She carried a 20mm Oerlikon but no radar. Note the fine shape of the bows due to the removal of the bow external tubes.

Plan view of a Group Three boat showing arrangement of the casing with the midships external tubes reversed.

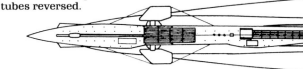

HMS *Thermopylae* on completion and fitted with 267PW radar, 138 ASDIC on the after casing and with a full shield enclosing the 4-inch gun.

▼**HMS *Triumph* at sea on 4 October 1940, showing her without the bow external tubes and fitted with a cab-type bridge.**
▶**HMS *Tigris* under refit at Devonport in June 1942.** the position for the 20mm Oerlikon gun can be seen at the after end of the conning tower. Although the gun has been fitted, the pedestal support has still to be plated over.

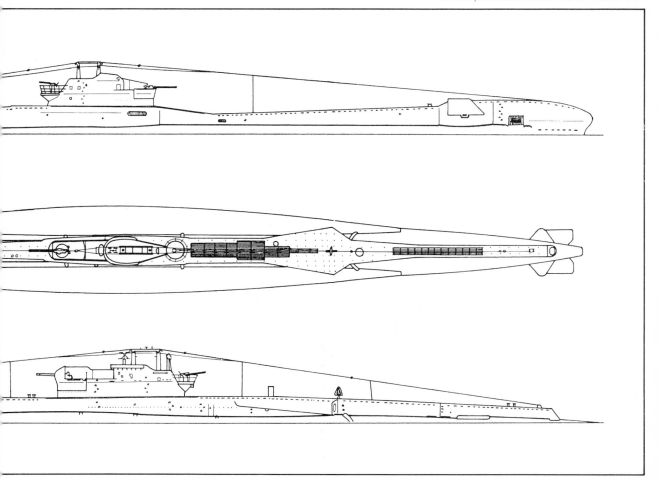

◄ HMS *Tigris* in Plymouth Sound in July 1942 on completion of refit. Features to note are the 20mm Oerlikon mounting, the DF coil on the after casing and the No. 11 stern tube. (IWM FL.3837)

► HMS *Torbay*, a similarly refitted Group One T boat in Plymouth Sound in November 1942. Unlike *Tigris*, however, *Torbay* has been fitted with 291W radar: the X-shaped aerial is visible between the Oerlikon and the periscope standards. (IWM FL.3438)

► HMS *Traveller* mooring stern-on to the jetty at Beirut on 1 October 1942 after a successful patrol off Benghazi. Note the reversed midships external tubes and the No. 11 stern tube. (IWM A.13131)

◄ A fine view of HMS *Thorn*, one of the seven Group Two T-class submarines, proceeding down the Mersey on completion in 1941. A shipyard offical stands rather self-consciously on the casing below the 4-inch gun. Note the much finer shape to the bow as a result of moving the bow externals aft. All Group Two boats had a cab bridge and their midship externals reversed to face aft as shown in this photograph. (IWM FL.4568)

► HMS *Thrasher*, one of only two Group Two boats to return from the Mediterranean, secured to a buoy in the Medway after refit on 29 May 1943. Alterations include the fitting of 291W radar, a 20mm Oerlikon and the removal of the cab in favour of an open bridge. (IWM FL.5817)

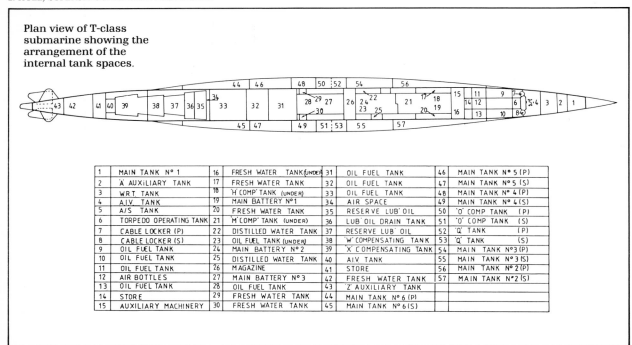

Plan view of T-class submarine showing the arrangement of the internal tank spaces.

1	MAIN TANK N° 1	16	FRESH WATER TANK (UNDER)	31	OIL FUEL TANK	46	MAIN TANK N° 5 (P)
2	'A' AUXILIARY TANK	17	FRESH WATER TANK	32	OIL FUEL TANK	47	MAIN TANK N° 5 (S)
3	W.R.T. TANK	18	'H' COMP' TANK (UNDER)	33	OIL FUEL TANK	48	MAIN TANK N° 4 (P)
4	A.I.V. TANK	19	MAIN BATTERY N° 1	34	AIR SPACE	49	MAIN TANK N° 4 (S)
5	A/S TANK	20	FRESH WATER TANK	35	RESERVE LUB' OIL	50	'O' COMP TANK (P)
6	TORPEDO OPERATING TANK	21	'M' COMP' TANK (UNDER)	36	LUB' OIL DRAIN TANK	51	'O' COMP TANK (S)
7	CABLE LOCKER (P)	22	DISTILLED WATER TANK	37	RESERVE LUB' OIL	52	'Q' TANK (P)
8	CABLE LOCKER (S)	23	OIL FUEL TANK (UNDER)	38	'W' COMPENSATING TANK	53	'Q' TANK (S)
9	OIL FUEL TANK	24	MAIN BATTERY N° 2	39	'X' COMPENSATING TANK	54	MAIN TANK N° 3 (P)
10	OIL FUEL TANK	25	DISTILLED WATER TANK	40	A.I.V TANK	55	MAIN TANK N° 3 (S)
11	OIL FUEL TANK	26	MAGAZINE	41	STORE	56	MAIN TANK N° 2 (P)
12	AIR BOTTLES	27	MAIN BATTERY N° 3	42	FRESH WATER TANK	57	MAIN TANK N° 2 (S)
13	OIL FUEL TANK	28	OIL FUEL TANK	43	'Z' AUXILIARY TANK		
14	STORE	29	FRESH WATER TANK	44	MAIN TANK N° 6 (P)		
15	AUXILIARY MACHINERY	30	FRESH WATER TANK	45	MAIN TANK N° 6 (S)		

reported going below this level although none could equal *Tetrarch*'s descent to 400 feet while under attack on 23 April 1940 (*see* Chapter 6).[17] Diving time was about 30 seconds from a 50 per cent buoyancy condition. Each boat had two sets of hydroplanes, one forward and one aft. The forward pair lay above the waterline and were hinged so that they could be turned in to avoid damage when entering harbour or in a heavy sea. The after pair were fixed in the down position below the waterline at the stern where they could best take advantage of the propeller wash. The hydroplanes were operated from the control room and driven by the ship's telemotor system. Arrangements existed for manual control should the telemotor system fail. Two T boats, *Triad* and *Taku*, suffered failures of their after planes from the same cause: the outboard mechanism failed and the planes jammed in an almost vertical position producing a Kitchen rudder effect whereby they were unable to make headway. *Triad*'s (Lieutenant-Commander E. R. J. Oddie) failure occurred in November 1939 off the Norwegian coast. The Norwegian authorities generously waived their rights as a neutral nation and allowed *Triad* to use facilities at Stavanger to make good the damage: she was hauled stern first up the slip on 1 December 1939 and by 1400 the next day was on her way home, the Norwegian Naval Chief of Staff having personally reconnoitred the route out of Stavanger to ensure that no German forces were lying in wait. *Taku*'s (Lieutenant J. F. 'Boy' Brown) failure occurred at sea in the Atlantic in February 1941 and she had to be towed back to Londonderry and then the Clyde by *Salvonia* and *Gladiolus*. *Taku* had to wait for nearly three days for the tow to arrive.[18]

Figure 2 shows the complicated maze of main, auxiliary, fuel and compensating tanks which lay below the main deck. A T boat had eleven main, or ballast, tanks: No. 1 tank in the bow of the submarine within the pressure hull and running the full width of the submarine together with five pairs of saddle tanks port and starboard numbered 2 to 6 and running forward to aft. The ballast tanks were fitted with Kingston valves at the bottom for flooding, outboard vents at the top, and blowing connections to the boat's HP air system. In the Group Three boats, 3 and 5 main tanks were converted to fuel tanks.

There were also two auxiliary tanks, A and Z, used for the quick adjustment of trim while diving, situated one each end of the submarine. A and Z tanks had telemotor-operated Kingston valves, HP air blows and could be vented inboard or outboard. Five compensating tanks, known as H, M, O, W and X tanks and running from forward to aft, were used to compensate changes in the submarine's weight as stores and fuel were consumed during a patrol and for diving in waters of different density. The compensating tanks were connected to the Main Line, which ran down the port side of the boat, by suction and flooding connections, LP blows, and were fitted with inboard vents but no Kingstons. Lastly there was Q tank situated slightly forward of amidships to make the boat definitely heavy when a quick dive from the surface was required or when changing depth rapidly. Q tank was blown from the HP air system, was flooded via Kingstons and had inboard and outboard vents. The tank was of especially rigid construction since it might well have to be blown at the maximum diving depth of the submarine.

The complete list of tanks, their position and capacities are given below – the figures are for *Truant*.

Tank	Position (Frame No.)	Capacity (tons)
Ballast Tanks:		
1	8–13	18.5
2 P&S*	34–58	52
3 P&S	59–71	56
4 P&S	71–86	52
5 P&S	86–97	49
6 P&S	97–115	38.6
Auxiliary, compensating and other tanks:		
A Auxiliary	13–16	12.2
Z Auxiliary	146–154	9.3
Q Diving Tank P&S	71–75	11.4
H Compensating	44–49	8.7
M Compensating	49–55	10.8
O Compensating P&S	75–79	11.3
W Compensating	121–124	2.8
X Compensating	124–133	6.5
Fresh and distilled water:		
1 Fresh Water	40–44	2.98
2 Fresh Water	44–54 Port Side	3.99
3 Fresh Water	44–45 Starboard Side	3.92
4 Fresh Water	138–146	7.56
1 Distilled Water	56–60 Port Side	1.74
2 Distilled Water	59–66 Starboard Side	2.93
3 Distilled Water	76–79	1.26
Other tanks:		
WRT	16–21	5.1
Automatic Inboard Vent (AIV)	21–25	3.7
Torpedo Overflow Tank (TOT)	25–28	7[19]

*P&S = Port and Starboard

Tanks were vented and flooded from the control room from a panel known as the 'blowing panel' situated in the starboard after corner and operated by the 'Outside' ERA – the ERA responsible for all machinery outside the engine room. The commanding officer relied on verbal reports from the Outside ERA that the various orders had been carried out and that the appropriate valves were open or closed as required, but in *Truncheon*'s (Lieutenant-Commander J. Coote) first post-war commission an American 'Christmas Tree' board was fitted: an illuminated panel from which the CO could tell at a glance which valves were open/closed and which tanks were empty/full.[20]

A T boat's main machinery consisted of diesel engines for use on the surface and electric motors for submerged drive. The propulsion system of a T boat was adequate and reliable rather than exceptional. There was considerable variety in the diesels employed in the class and the various yards had considerable latitude. Thus Vickers-built boats used a Vickers engine, boats built in one or other of the Royal Dockyards were fitted with Admiralty engines, Cammell Laird-built boats had Sulzer engines and the early Scotts-built boats had German, supercharged MAN diesels although *Tabard*, the last of the Scotts-built T boats, was completed with Admiralty engines.

The diesels were arranged on two shafts and each was capable of producing 1,250bhp for a top speed of between 14–15 knots. *Triton* achieved a speed of 16.29 knots[21] on her first of class trials. This speed was not equalled by any other T boat, and after the declaration

▶ A fine view of HMS *Tally-Ho* passing through the Great Bitter Lakes in 1943 on her way to join the 4th Submarine Flotilla. The photograph shows most of the features common to Group Three submarines: almost flush line to the casing; open bridge; Oerlikon platform; radar and the three-tube stern salvo. (IWM A.31033)

of war, complaints from commanding officers began to come in regarding lack of speed on the surface. It would seem that 15 knots was the best a T-boat commander could hope for. The staff histories are littered with references to lack of speed leading to missed opportunities, although one of the most galling incidents concerned *Turbulent* (Commander J. W. Linton) at the end of 1942. The submarine was on patrol off Cagliari when a report was received from *Umbra* (Lieutenant S. L. S. Maydon) that three Italian *Littorio*-class battleships were at sea. Vice-Admiral Sir Anthony Troup, then serving as *Turbulent*'s First Lieutenant, recalled that: 'We had an enemy report that they were making up to the north. We were placed somewhere up in the middle of the Tyrrhenian Sea and in order to intercept the battle fleet we had to streak across and this was where our 15 knots didn't do us much good. We actually crossed about 6 miles astern of them or even less than that, for we went across their wake and got all the funnel fumes blown down on us . . . there was absolutely nothing we could do.'[22]

Yet despite the criticisms of lack of speed, the T class met the requirements for which they had been designed. During the pre-war period, British submariners did not see a high surface speed as particularly important – unlike their German counterparts.

It was the Vickers 6-cylinder, 4-stroke 1,250bhp engine that was fitted to the majority of the submarines in the class. It was a solid injection engine and somewhat primitive compared with the diesels used in German U-boats, but practical and easy to maintain. If a cylinder failed it could be disconnected from the crankshaft while the engine continued to run. In

Triton's first of class trials, the commanding officer reported that the Vickers diesels were 'exceptionally easy to operate'.[23] The Admiralty engine fitted in the twelve Dockyard-built boats was likewise reliable although it was considered somewhat more complicated to operate than the Vickers engine. The Vickers engine had a single fuel pump for the whole engine whereas Admiralty engines had one pump for each cylinder which had to be individually regulated causing more work for the engine room watchkeepers.

The same, however, could not be said for the MAN diesels fitted in the Scotts-built boats or the Sulzer's fitted to those Ts built by Cammell Laird. The MAN engines were built under licence by Scotts and once war was declared in 1939 the supply of advice and spare parts from the German parent company was terminated. It was sometimes sarcastically suggested that Scotts' German advisers had not been quite as forthcoming about these engines as they might! *Tribune* developed problems with the securing bolts for the cylinders and had to return to the UK from Canada with the diesels temporarily secured with pit props. *Tribune*'s First Lieutenant, now Vice-Admiral Sir John Roxburgh, commented that the 'MAN diesels in *Tribune* were a misery . . . we finally left Halifax with a whole lot of pit props holding down the cylinders jammed between the deckhead and the top of the cylinder with wooden wedges driven in. You could see these cylinders moving up and down even though we had the pit props holding them down.'[24]

The pit props were the idea of Warrant Engineer Bill Allin, *Tribune*'s engineer officer, and the submarine's engine room must have presented a most unusual

◀
P.311 on completion in 1942: the only boat not to receive a name. Note the absence of a hump in the casing around the midships external tubes. *P.311* and *Trespasser* were the only Group Three boats to complete without an Oerlikon.

◀
HMS *Tabard*, last of the class to complete, in 1946, and showing the final evolution of the design: compare this view with that of *Triumph* at the beginning of the chapter.

▶
An interesting post-war view of *Totem* showing the modified shape of the orifices of the bow external tubes. Compare this view with that of *Tribune* in 2. Note also the hydroplanes turned out to allow ratings to work on the casing.

appearance! By 1943 only *Tribune* and *Tuna* survived of the MAN-engined boats and both were withdrawn from operations and used for trials and training purposes. In March 1944, when there was a critical shortage of boats in the Far East, Admiral (Submarines) declined to send *Tuna* on the grounds that 'she is fitted with a foreign engine which we do not trust far from home'.[25]

Views about the Sulzer engines were divided. *Thorn's* First Lieutenant described them as 'perfectly successful'[26] and *Thrasher's* commanding officer remarked that: 'I thought they were super. They didn't give much trouble and were much quieter. They purred like a sewing-machine as opposed to clattering like a bus. They seemed to make less noise and were smoother running.'[27] In fact *Thrasher* went through the war with remarkably few mechanical problems. After her return from the Mediterranean, she did a second commission in Home Waters, followed by a third in the Far East, and was one of only three British submarines to serve in all three theatres of operations – the other two were *Trident* and *Truant*. The main problem with the 2-stroke Sulzer engines was that they were over-rated in the engineering sense and lack sufficient margins of power

when running at full speed. Consequently the cylinder rings started to crack followed by the cylinder blocks. In the Mediterranean *Taku's* commanding officer, Lieutenant Arthur Pitt, reckoned that in every 1,000 miles of running at least one engine would be unavailable because the engine staff were having to lift a piston. She eventually returned to the UK with two pistons slung.[28] *Trident* suffered similar problems and after going out to Ceylon in 1943 developed engine problems while on patrol off Sumatra and had to return home to the UK.[29]

A 336-cell battery split into three sections drove two 1,450bhp Laurence Scott electric motors for submerged drive. Each motor consisted of two armatures on each shaft. The armatures could be set to run in parallel for high speed ('Group Up') or in series ('Group Down'). Nos. 1 and 2 battery sections lay adjacent to each other beneath the accommodation area while No. 3 battery lay under the control room. Each cell weighed more than half a ton and at sea had to be topped up regularly with distilled water. Fully charged the battery could provide power for almost 48 hours' dived endurance at a speed of 2½ knots. At their top dived speed of

▶ HMS *Triad* in Maestri Fiord, Stavanger, on 1 December 1939 following the failure of her after hydroplanes. The submarine is trimmed down by the bow in order to bring the after planes nearer the surface and thus lessen the Kitchen rudder effect.

▶▼ CERA Rogers finishes repair work on 'Q' inboard vent on board HMS *Tempest*.

▼ HMS *Tiptoe* at Barrow in June 1944, the first T-class submarine of all-welded construction. Note the prominent aerial for the American SJ radar at the after end of the periscope standards.

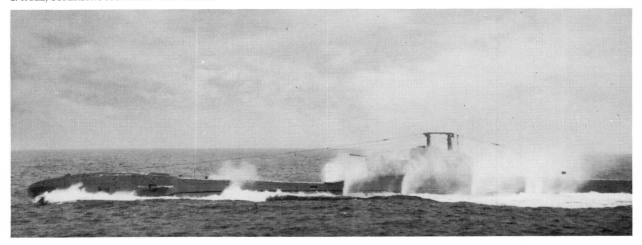

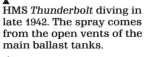

▲
HMS *Thunderbolt* diving in late 1942. The spray comes from the open vents of the main ballast tanks.

◄
Tapir being broken up at Faslane in 1967. The photograph was taken from over No. 3 battery compartment looking forward into the remains of the accommodation space. The circular line of the pressure hull can be seen together with the saddle tanks on each side. The top of the pressure hull has been lifted to assist the removal of large items of equipment. (Dr. Ian Buxton)

◄
HMS *Telemachus* in dry dock at Sydney, Australia in 1951, showing the rudder, starboard propeller and after hydroplane. At the top right is an open aperture for No. 9 torpedo tube. (Gus Britton)

►
Tribune's engine room showing the troublesome MAN diesels. (IWM A.10922)

9 knots the battery would give out after little more than one hour. It was soon apparent that the batteries were very vulnerable to shock damage as a result of depth-charge or air attack, *Truant* and *Thrasher* being just two of the T boats that reported battery damage after being attacked; the latter reporting only 30 out of 336 cells intact after being attacked in July 1942. The solution lay in the fitting of strengthened battery containers and rubber envelopes and pads for each battery cell to cushion it against shock and this seemed to cure the problem. *Taku*'s (Lieutenant-Commander A. J. Pitt) battery successfully withstood the explosion of a mine overhead in April 1944, while *Terrapin*'s (Lieutenant R. H. Brunner) reported that his battery was undamaged in the severe hammering the boat received from the Japanese in May 1945 which resulted in her being written off as a constructive total loss.[30]

Auxiliary machinery comprised the telemotor system, ballast pumps and the HP air system. The telemotor system was responsible for the quick and silent operation of the submarine's hydroplanes, vents, Kingstons, rudders, periscope, radar and W/T masts, bow caps and engine induction valves. T boats were fitted with two Vickers 5hp reciprocating telemotor pumps which were reliable but very noisy. Successful trials with a silent, screw-type IMO pump in *Tetrarch* led to one of the Vickers pumps being removed and replaced by an IMO-type pump for use as an 'attack' pump both during and after an attack. Other improvements to the system included the insistence on better workmanship and quality control in the manufacture of the pump, the fitting of a 10–15lb air lead to the telemotor replenishment tank to boost suction, increasing the pump suction from 1¼in bore to 2in bore

and the fitting of filters in the oil supply lines. After 1942, one Vickers 10hp and one IMO 32–9 (1,450rpm) pumps were fitted to all submarines, including Ts, as part of a standardization programme.

T boats were originally fitted with three ballast pumps, one forward and two aft, although one of the after pair was omitted in Group Three boats to speed up production. Vessels from *Triton* to the three 1938 Programme boats had centrex pumps which, like the early telemotor system, were reliable but noisy. All Group Two and Three boats were fitted with rotary centrex pumps after trials in *Tribune* had shown it to be less noisy. The pumps could discharge 100 tons per hour at 30 feet and 10 tons per hour at 300 feet although

many boats reported problems with discharging water at depths below 200 feet. *Triumph* was fitted with one experimental Worthington Simpson ballast pump which her CO (Commander W. Woods) reported 'had consistently given trouble'.[31]

A T-class boat had two air systems: High (HP) and Low (LP) Pressure. HP air was required for blowing ballast tanks when surfacing and for firing torpedoes. But HP air was precious and so, once the submarine was buoyant, LP air was used to attain full buoyancy. The LP air system could also be used for compartment testing or salvage blowing while on the surface. HP air was stored at 4,000psi in seventeen bottles in four groups: No. 1 Group consisting of five bottles and the

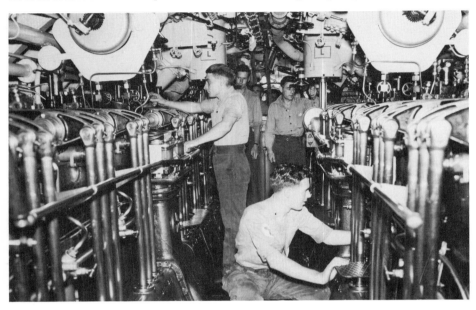

Routine cleaning duties in *Thorough's* engine room in the early 1950s. *Thorough*, a Vickers-built boat, had two 1,250bhp Vickers engines.

Rear-Admiral Viscount Kelburn, Flag Officer Malta, inspects *Token's* extremely clean engine room in February 1962 after the submarine had recommissioned. Note the covers in place over the rocker arms of the Admiralty engines.

others of four bottles each, giving a total volume of 161.5cu. ft. The air groups could be used individually or collectively to supply air to the main HP ring main or to the main blowing panel. The groups would be recharged while on the surface by running the two motor-driven compressors both located aft in the auxiliary machinery space. Two LP air blowers were fitted, one forward and one aft, which took their suction from the atmosphere and discharged into the LP line through a non-return valve.

Leaks from the HP air system were quite normal and a pressure always built up in the boat during a day's dive, but the HP system was acutely vulnerable to shock damage. In *Talisman* (Lieutenant-Commander M.

Willmott) on 22 October 1940, the air pipe to No. 1 group was smashed when No. 6 reload torpedo broke loose following an outboard explosion, slid aft and hit the pipe causing a pressure of some 12psi to build up in the boat. When Willmott attempted to open the conning tower hatch, both clips smashed and the hatch was severely distorted.[32] *Zwaardvis* (Lieutenant-Commander H. A. W. Goossens) reported that the air pipe to No. 3 group was smashed in a depth-charge attack in December 1944.[33]

The lessons of over-complicated machinery had been learned the hard way in the O, P and R classes: a T boat's main and auxiliary machinery though not outstanding was practical, reliable and easy to maintain.

▶
Tribune's motor room in 1942, showing the two switchboards controlling the electric motors. Note also the engine room telegraphs: astern power was possible only on the motors. (IWM A.10898)

▶
A contrasting view of *Token*'s motor room in 1962.

3. Torpedoes, Guns and Mines

With a forward-firing salvo of ten 21in torpedo tubes, the T class possessed the largest salvo of any submarine in the world. The six internal tubes were fitted in two banks of three, numbered top to bottom: 1, 3 and 5 on the starboard side and 2, 4 and 6 on the port side. The external tubes were numbered 7 and 8 for the bow pair and 9 and 10 for the midships pair: as with the internal tubes, even numbers were on the port side, odd numbers on the starboard side.[1] Each tube was fitted with a hydraulically operated bow cap which was worked by a ram powered from the telemotor system. Each ram was independently operated and was so configured that a force of approximately 14,000lb could be brought to bear on the cap by the hydraulic cylinder working at 1,500psi. Interlocks were fitted to the bow cap equipment and the firing gear to prevent a torpedo being fired while the bow cap was shut. The bow caps were protected by orifices or bow shutters in way of the tube openings. Bow shutters had not been fitted in *Oberon* or subsequent construction, but their reintroduction for the Ts seems to have been the result of an unsubstantiated report that the Portuguese submarine *Golphino* had achieved 1½ knots above trial speed with bow shutters fitted. The shutters were fitted to the shell-plating orifices in way of the tube openings for the six internal tubes. They were geared with the bow caps so that the latter could not be worked until the shutter was fully open. In the event bow shutters were only fitted to *Triton, Thetis, Triumph, Trident, Tribune, Thistle, Taku, Tarpon* and *Triad*; they were a doubtful feature and were very prone to being blocked by flotsam. In *Truant* and subsequent boats, the bow shutters were omitted and the orifices reshaped so as to minimize the loss of speed which was in the order of ½-knot on the surface and .15-knot dived. Removing the bow shutters also required that interlocks be fitted to prevent the bow cap and rear door being open at the same time. These interlocks were first fitted in *Talisman* and *Torbay*.[2]

The rear door of each internal tube was opened by a lever-operated quick-acting mechanism consisting of counter-rotating interlocking lugs. The face of the rear door was fitted with a test cock which allowed the crew to test whether or not the tube was full of water. A 4-inch-long brass rimer was provided so that the test cock could be kept clear of obstructions. There was also a drain fitted to the rear door which allowed water in the tube to be emptied into the bilges. After the loss of *Thetis* as a result of the rear door to No. 5 tube being

opened while the bow cap was open, the rear doors were fitted with a safety clip which became known as the 'Thetis clip'. It consisted of a single butterfly nut which was only released after the lever had been worked and prevented the door opening more than a fraction should the bow cap be open or the tube be full of water.

Between the two banks of internal tubes were the bow-cap indicators which showed whether or not the bow cap was open, and were directly connected to the operating rams. There were also six indicators, one for each tube, which showed when the bow cap was fully open. Those for 2, 4 and 6 tubes were on the port side of the tube space and those for 1, 3 and 5 tubes on the

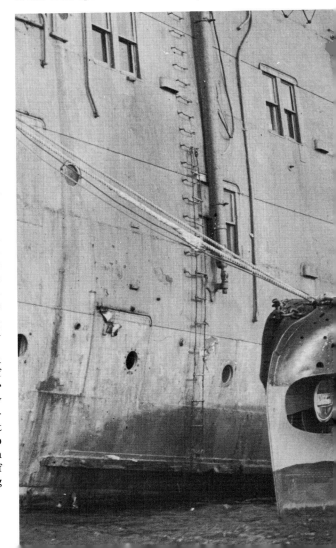

► A view of *Thetis* after salvage, showing eight of the ten forward firing torpedo tubes. Note the shutters covering the orifices for the six internal tubes.

▼ *Tuna* alongside the depot ship *Exmouth* at Scapa Flow on 29 September 1943, showing the bow cap for No. 8 open with a torpedo visible in the tube. The submarine is riding fairly light in the water: note the aperture for No. 2 tube and that the bow shutters are no longer fitted. (IWM A.19546)

starboard side. When the bow cap was fully open a tell-tale showed the legend 'Safe to Fire'.

Each T boat carried six reload torpedoes in the torpedo-stowage compartment. The torpedoes were lowered nose first into the compartment through the torpedo loading hatch. Torpedoes for the top and middle pairs of tubes were stowed in trolleys, two a side one above the other, which were pulled out from the bulkhead until they lined up with the torpedo tube. The trolley was locked in position and supported on portable transverse rails which could be easily rigged and dismantled as required. The torpedo was then pushed forward along the trolley into the tube using block and tackle. Portable transverse supports were fitted between bulkhead 25 and the breech end of the tube to support the torpedo when its weight came off the trolley and before it was taken by the side lugs in the tube. Torpedoes for the lower pair were stowed on simple trolleys moving fore and aft on rails set in the deck. Stowage was supposed to be secure, but occasionally torpedoes came adrift in heavy weather. In November 1940 *Trident*'s No. 4 reload torpedo came adrift while the boat was rolling in heavy weather and ended up lying diagonally across the compartment.[3]

The torpedoes were loaded by hand. However, in the summer of 1939 *Triumph* experimented with a power loading system which had been developed in the minelayer *Grampus* using the hydraulic torpedo lifting press thus: '. . . shackling a purchase on to the torpedo lifting wire, the standing part being connected to an eye in the bottom of the trenches. This wire, known as the "loading wire" is led aft through a block connected to the after bulkhead of the torpedo compartment and then brought forward and shackled on to the launching in wire of the torpedo. The torpedo is then loaded by working the lifting press.'[4] The trials were unsuccessful largely because the press lacked sufficient power to haul the torpedo right home. *Triumph*'s commanding officer recommended that they be continued using stronger blocks, but RA(S) disagreed. The debate continued until 14 December 1939 when it was decided not to take the matter further since 'with the severe cutting down of the time in working up submarines it appears undesirable to delay a submarine for these purposes'.[5]

During the Second World War the loading arrangements for torpedoes were simplified. The transporter trolleys, with their rather insecure strops, were replaced by bracket stowage with hinged arms so that the torpedoes were merely 'skidded' into the loading position.[6]

The firing of a torpedo was a complex operation since each torpedo, in the case of a Mk VIII**, weighed 1,566kg and unless correct trim was maintained after firing the submarine was likely to make an unscheduled appearance in full view of the opposition. To prevent this there was an elaborate system of compensating tanks and valves. Once each torpedo had been loaded, the tube was 'blown up' with water from the WRT (Water Round Torpedo) tank: the amount of water required being the

difference between the capacity of the tube and the displacement of the torpedo; in a T boat this meant nearly half a ton of water had to be blown into the tube. The torpedo was then fired by air impulse. If the air were allowed to follow the torpedo out of the tube the discharge splash on the surface would give the submarine's position away. Therefore once the torpedo had impetus but was still in the tube the AIV (Automatic Inboard Vent) valve allowed the air to come back into an open tank which also received the amount of water representing the difference between the weight of the torpedo and the corresponding volume of water. Once the torpedo was clear, the tube filled with water which, after the bow cap was shut, was drained down into the TOT tanks (Torpedo Overflow Tanks) which held the amount of water in the torpedo tube in excess of the capacity of the WRT tank.

The four external tubes were a new feature as far as British submarine practice in the inter-war period went, and allowed a greater torpedo armament to be carried without weakening the hull structure with too many openings. The tube was known as the 'E'-type tube and for ease of operation it was fitted with a 5° bow down angle in all boats except *Triton*.[7] The operating arrangements for the external tubes were somewhat

◀
The rear doors to Nos. 2
and 4 tubes in an
unidentified T-class
submarine, showing the
opening arrangements:
the quick-acting opening
lever is on the right; the
safety or *'Thetis'* clip is on
the left of the door.

▶
A rating at the torpedo
firing position in the tube
space between the two
banks of torpedo tubes.
The indicators above his
head relay the torpedo
tube orders given in the
control room. (IWM
D.12478)

▶
A torpedo, in this case a
Mk VIII*E, being swung
into position prior to
loading into *Thrasher*'s No.
8 tube. Note the gratings
lifted up from the casing
to give access to the rear
end of the tube.

▶
Traveller's fore-ends
showing the portable
transverse loading rails in
position with the reload
torpedo for No. 2 tube on
its trolley pulled out into
the loading position. (IWM
A.13136)

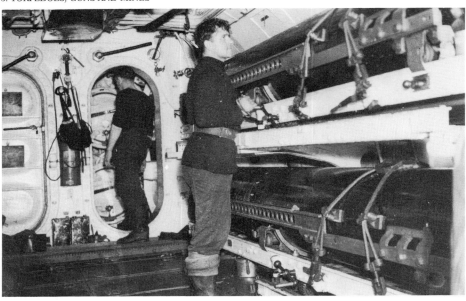

Early torpedo stowage arrangements in *Thrasher*: note the torpedoes secured by wire strops.

Thunderbolt, ex-*Thetis*, fires a practice shot using a tethered torpedo from No. 9 tube in Malta on 15 February 1943. (IWM A.14631)

Compare the previous photograph with this 1950s view of a Mk VIII** in *Telemachus*' fore-ends. The strops have been replaced by bracket stowage: those for Nos. 1 and 3 tubes are seen in the 'up' position. When 'down' they supported the torpedo in the loading position. (Gus Britton)

The 'Fruit Machine': an electrically driven mechanical fire control computer for the torpedo armament situated at the forward end of the control room. It did not generate a continuous solution and had to be reset after each periscope observation. (IWM A.22331)

different since, naturally, they could not be loaded from within the boat. Access to the rear door of the tube was gained by lifting gratings in the casing, the torpedo was then loaded in the normal fashion. The bow-cap was hand-operated from within the submarine. Many commanding officers complained that the rod gearing for opening the bow-cap was often stiff and required considerable effort to work it: Charles Deleay, an LTO in *Tantalus* (Lieutenant-Commander H. S. Mackenzie), remembers the rod breaking away as he tried to close the bow-cap to the No. 11 tube.[8]

Linked with the hand-operating gear were watertight cocks, one per tube, which allowed the tube to be flooded up, thus equalizing pressure on the bow cap.

Once the external tubes were loaded the torpedo could not simply be withdrawn for maintenance: the only way to deal with a recalcitrant torpedo in an external tube while on patrol was to fire it as safely as possible. In March 1942 *Torbay* (Commander A. C. C. Miers) was returning to base when it was found that the securing pin of No. 8 tube had sheared and that the torpedo had eased itself out of the tube about half its length. The torpedo was dangerous and had to be disposed of since the fan had unwound, cocking the pistol. After *Torbay*'s engineer officer had failed to shift the torpedo with a crowbar, Miers disposed of the menace by firing the torpedo while diving the submarine at full speed astern.[9] The external tubes were also vulnerable to

damage: in *Truant* the torpedoes in the bow externals sheared their securing pins and fell out of the tubes, without the warheads exploding, when what was thought to be a magnetic mine exploded alongside.[10]

The torpedo for which all this equipment was designed was the Mk VIII of which the principal variant was the Mk VIII**. Despite inflated claims about the efficiency of German torpedoes, the facts are that the 21in Mk VIII** with its 'Brotherhood' burner cycle engine, range of 4,570 metres at 45.5 knots (or 6,400 metres at 41 knots) and warhead of 365kg of Torpex had greater propulsive efficiency than any contemporary torpedo of similar size. However, shortages of this weapon in the early days of the war meant that some

submarines went to war with the older Mk IV torpedo. A variant of this weapon, the Mk VIII*E, was developed for use in external tubes and had smaller propellers and lacked the 45.5-knot speed setting.

The Mk VIII was initially fitted with a contact pistol which detonated the warhead when the torpedo struck the target. Evidence suggested that greater damage would be caused if the explosion occurred directly under the target, so the non-contact CCR (Compensated Coil Rod) magnetic pistol was introduced which fired the warhead as the torpedo passed beneath the target. The CCR pistol gave endless problems and was eventually withdrawn. Perhaps the most mortifying setback as a result of faulty CCR pistols occurred when *Thule*

(Lieutenant A. C. G. Mars) fired all three stern tubes at a Japanese *RO.100*-class submarine off Penang. When Mars raised his periscope he was rewarded with the sight of a column of water in the air and the submarine's stern rising to the vertical. He thought he had been successful and accordingly a 'U' symbol was sewn on *Thule*'s 'Jolly Roger'. Post-war analysis, however, indicated that what Mars had seen was the premature explosion of one of the CCR-fitted torpedoes and the upraised stern was the Japanese boat performing one of the quickest dives in submarine history.

During the post-war period it was intended that the Mk VIIIs should be replaced by the Mk XX(S) 'Bidder' electric passive homing torpedo and the Mk XII 'Fancy' HTP torpedo. However, the Mk XII was withdrawn after the *Sidon* tragedy[11] while the Mk XX(S) was abandoned after 75 had been manufactured by Vickers. Its replacement was the Mk XXIII wire-guided torpedo which, although tested in 1955 and ordered in 1959, was not cleared for front-line use until 1971! Throughout this depressing saga of torpedo development, the Mk VIII remained the mainstay of a T boat's armament (*see* Appendix 2 for specifications of all these weapons).

Compared with the equipment in a German U-boat, British torpedo fire control was very primitive. German U-boats possessed a fire control computer which generated a continuous solution and did not have to be reset after each periscope observation. British attack instruments were sufficient, but rudimentary and everything depended on the skill of the commanding officer. British torpedoes could not be continually angled so the boat had to be pointed ahead of the target and wait for the DA (Director Angle) to come on. This required quick descents to below periscope depth for a burst of high speed on the best-known track for the

target's last-known course: a last-minute alteration of course by the target could ruin the whole attack. The range and bearing of the target were taken by observation through the periscope – which had a gunnery-type coincidence rangefinder. The observations were then 'entered' on either an 'ISWAS' – a rudimentary DA calculator – or the 'fruit machine' – an electrically driven mechanical fire control computer – which replaced the ISWAS and which produced the DA. Both suffered from the same fault: they could not generate a continuous track and had to be reset after each periscope observation. Firing using a bearing provided by ASDIC was possible but simply did not work in action. For firing torpedoes on the surface, there were two simple sights on the bridge although these were totally inferior to comparable German equipment.

Something more refined was required for the T Conversions and Streamlines in the post-war fleet, yet the story of fire control development is as depressing as that of the torpedo. TCS(S)3 (Torpedo Control System (Submarines) Mk 3) was intended for fitting in the Conversions and Streamlines. It consisted of a Mk 3 torpedo director automatically provided with information from ASDIC, radar, periscope observation and the time/bearing plot, and capable of setting running depths and gyro angles on the torpedoes in the tubes. However, it was criticized for not being able to generate a continually updated solution, for being hideously complicated to operate and for being unable to apply a gyro angle of greater than 70° to the torpedoes in the tubes. Delays in production meant that TCS(S)3 did not appear until the summer of 1954 when it was fitted in *Thermopylae* for trials, although the first T Conversion to receive an operational set was *Tabard* in May 1955.[12] In the meantime the geriatric TCS(S)2Mod.1 was used

which was little better than the wartime 'fruit machine'.

T boats also carried a 4in gun which was fitted as a weapon of surprise and also for self-defence if unable to dive. Positioning the gun was a matter of compromise. Since it was a weapon of surprise the gun had to be as high as possible in order to bring it quickly into action, but conditions of stability and silhouette limited the height at which it could be placed. The gun-tower hatch had to be a reasonable height above the water-line when the submarine was in the lowest buoyancy condition and the gun tower itself had to be of such a height that the ammunition number inside could stand easily between the upper and lower hatches otherwise the passage of ammunition would be slowed. The weapon was positioned in an open breastwork mounting above the casing and forward of the conning tower. Other than the waist-high breastwork, no shield or protective plating was fitted because of weight considerations. During the war many T boat commanders, notably Commander W. King of *Trusty* and *Telemachus*,[13] petitioned for additional armour plating around the conning tower and gun position, but their requests were always refused. Nevertheless, the need for protection was eventually recognized. In the Far East the depot ships manufactured crude 'half shields' around the gun position to provide the crew with some protection. *Tabard*, *Talent* and *Teredo* were completed with full shields which completely enclosed the gun and gave adequate protection to most of the crew and which were subsequently fitted to all the remaining boats.

The Mk XII 4in gun was the weapon fitted in most T boats although *Trusty*, *Tapir*, *Talent*, *Templar* and *Tijgerhaai* were completed with the Mk XXII, and *Tally-Ho*, *Teredo*, *Tabard* and *Thermopylae* were refitted with this weapon after the war. Both the Mk XII and the Mk XXII were an interchangeable series of guns for use on the S1 mounting. During the post-war period the number of spare barrels for the Mk XII/XXII began to dwindle so those boats that retained their gun armament were armed with the Mk XXIII gun which had a shorter barrel than the Mk XII/XXII and carried a prominent recuperator cylinder above the barrel.

The Mk XII/XXII had a crew of five: gunlayer, breechworker, sightsetter, trainer and loader. Ready-use lockers in the superstructure held five rounds each, but there was also a 'human chain' of ratings in the gun tower to pass ammunition from the magazine, situated directly beneath the wardroom and reached via a hatch in the passageway, to the gun position. The allowance of ammunition allocated to T boats, 100 rounds, was found to be insufficient during the war and increases were authorized to allow for stowage of greater numbers, and varieties, of shell including HE (high-explosive), SAP (semi-armour piercing) and star-shell. By the end of the war T boats were going to sea without some reload torpedoes: the racks in the fore ends being filled with additional 4in and 20mm ammunition.

Gun action was the antithesis of submarine warfare since the submarine had to surface thereby giving away her main asset – invisibility. Nevertheless, gun action was exciting and offered almost instant results with little or no chance of retribution from the carefully chosen target. Once the target had been sighted the captain would manoeuvre for a favourable attacking position: one or two thousand yards aft of the target's beam was considered most advantageous. While doing so the gunlayer and trainer would be given the oppor-

◄
HMS *Thule*'s ship's company poses proudly with their 'Jolly Roger' in 1945: note the 'U' symbol for the attack on a Japanese submarine on 28 December 1944, frustrated by a faulty CCR pistol.

►
The shape of things to come: *Truncheon* fires a Mk XX from No. 2 tube while dived in Stokes Bay on 25 October 1966. The torpedo had its rudders locked 'up' and was fired using normal impulse to examine the feasibility of launching airflight weapons from a standard torpedo tube.

tunity to inspect their victim through the periscope before joining the rest of the gun's crew in the gun tower. The boat was then taken to 60 feet while the First Lieutenant bled HP air into the boat until a pressure of a few inches above atmospheric pressure was reached. The motors were put to 'Half Ahead Group Up' to give the hydroplanes maximum effect and the captain ordered 'Surface!' All tanks were blown, with the hydroplanes holding the boat down. When the boat had risen to approximately 30 feet and could no longer be held down against the increasing positive buoyancy, the First Lieutenant blew a whistle: the planesmen put the hydroplanes to 'hard-a-rise'; the gunlayer removed the last clip from the hatch and the gun's crew scrambled out, propelled upwards through the hatch by the excess pressure inside the boat. The essence of the whole operation was speed: *Trident*'s gun crew had the first round away within 30 seconds of the order to surface being given,[14] although *Terrapin* recorded bringing their gun into action in 22 seconds when dealing with a Japanese submarine-chaser.[15]

The rate of fire was one round every ten seconds and it would not be long before the target was disabled or sunk. Securing after a gun action was equally rapid: it did not pay for a submarine to remain on the surface admiring her handiwork. Fire control was entirely visual, the gunnery officer on the bridge would pass simple corrections down to the gun position by shouting over the front of the bridge or via the voicepipe. However, some boats experimented with using their Type 291W radar for fire control: in open waters it

worked quite well, but it was subject to too much clutter and back echoes in inshore waters to be of much use.

Submarines also carried three .303 Lewis machine-guns which, from 1941 onwards, were replaced by the more robust and efficient .303 gas-operated Vickers machine-gun which were described as 'very success-ful.'[16] The .303 Bren gun was a useful substitute if supplies could be obtained from the Army. Considera-tion was also given to fitting the T boats with a more substantial close-range AA gun. The favoured weapon was the 20mm Oerlikon. In February 1942 Constructor Commander A. C. Sims, the Constructor on the staff of Admiral (Submarines) wrote, 'It is either Oerlikon or nothing.'[17]

The ubiquitous 20mm Oerlikon was a useful sub-marine weapon though not as successful in the AA role

Plan view of HMS *Tetrarch* showing the layout of the mine wells on the saddle tanks port and starboard.

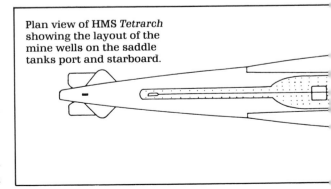

◄
The 4-inch Mk XII gun in
an S.1 breastwork
mounting in HMS *Taurus*.
(IWM A.21521)

▶
Additional 4-inch
ammunition being stowed
in the reload rack for No. 4
tube in *Trump* in the Far
East in 1945. The
authorities at Whale
Island might not have
approved, but the
additional stowage was
necessary since there
were few targets worth a
torpedo. (Royal Navy
Submarine Museum)

▶
Close-range weapons, in
this case a Vickers' gas-
operated machine-gun, on
the starboard side of
Terrapin's bridge. (IWM
A.28136)

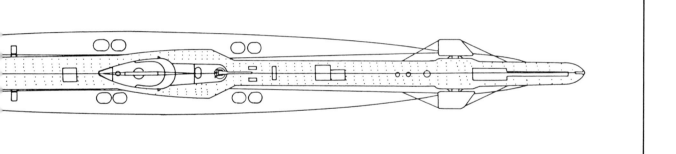

as expected. The weapon had a crew of two: a gunner and loader who supplied the ammunition contained in 'pans', each one holding 120 rounds. The gunner stood in a stepped well at the after end of the conning tower which allowed him to increase the weapon's elevation by stepping down. Safety rails prevented an over-enthusiastic gunner from damaging the bridge and killing the bridge personnel. It was believed to have considerable deterrent value and was useful for shooting up junks and light craft in the Far East. But the weapon had various problems: it was prone to jamming and the cartwheel sight was less than accurate against fast-moving targets. On the whole, the weapon was fairly well liked. *Tactician*'s Oerlikon gunner compared his weapon to a woman: 'plenty of attention, no neglect, she would not let you down'.[18]

In the Far East where there were few targets worth a torpedo, there was a demand for greater firepower and many T boat commanding officers resorted to their own solutions to this problem. *Terrapin* (Lieutenant R. H. H. Brunner) acquired an air-cooled .5in Browning machine-gun which must have been hideously awkward to manhandle up the conning tower with its belt ammunition, but which possessed immense stopping-power. However, the weight of this weapon proved too much for the relatively 'soft' brass conning-tower structure which began to buckle and the Browning had to go.[19] *Tantivy* carried two single Oerlikons side by side in the bandstand supported on pedestals which went down to the saddle tanks. *Tireless* completed with two Oerlikons on a twin Mk 12A mounting, but she was the only boat to carry such a weapon.[20]

In December 1944/January 1945 Commander J. W. Maitland, RN, Admiral (Submarines) gunnery officer, visited the British submarines operating in the Far East and reported that: '. . . chief impression which I bring back from the British flotillas is the strongly expressed desire for increased hitting power and, in particular, the provision of better ahead covering fire from some automatic gun capable of effective fire at 3,000 yards' range.'[21]

One of the options discussed was to convert a T-class submarine to a 'gun submarine' by removing some of the torpedo armament, but the plan was rejected because 'such a boat would be too slow on the surface'.[22] However Maitland's report resulted in a submission to the Admiralty by Admiral (Submarines) on 14 February 1945 that the 6pdr 7cwt gun should be fitted on the casing aft between 9 and 10 tubes. The 40mm Bofors gun was considered, but 'the difficulty of maintaining it efficiently under submarine conditions are considered sufficient to preclude its adoption'.[23] In order to compensate for the additional top weight the bow external torpedo tubes would have to be removed together with the DF coil, 4in RU lockers in the conning tower and the torpedo loading derricks. In the event such modifications would not be necessary since delays in production meant it would be a considerable time before the mounting were available in any quantity. However, *Tantivy* is believed to have been fitted with this weapon following a refit at Chatham Dockyard in 1945 although no drawings or photographs exist to confirm this.

Guns were not fitted to any of the T Conversions, but made a reappearance in the streamlined *Tapir*, *Talent* and *Token* in the shape of a single Mk XXIII on a pedestal mounting, without a shield, forward of the conning tower. It was but a brief renaissance: the gun was useful for low-intensity operations but had little place in the anti-submarine war which became the Royal Navy's main priority during the post-war era.

The third weapon in a T-boat's armoury was the mine. *Tetrarch*, *Torbay* and *Talisman*, the three boats of the 1938 Programme, were designed to lay mines

◀▶
The guns' crews of
Trenchant (left) and
Terrapin (right) at
Trincomalee on 20 March
1945 after a joint patrol in
which both boats sank the
special S/M Chaser No. 5
in a combined gun action
together with a number of
smaller vessels. When
Terrapin's ammunition
ran out she exhanged 100
dozen fresh eggs taken
from a captured coaster
for 60 rounds of
Trenchant's 4-inch
ammunition. *Trenchant*'s
crew (rear row left to
right): Leading Stoker H. I.
Stephens; Lieutenant P.
Cullen, RNVR; Able
Seaman J. Sowerby;
Leading Seaman F. Gavin.
Front row: PO G. Jacques;
Petty Officer J. A.
Lawrence; and Able
Seaman R. Broadbent.
Terrapin's crew (rear row
left to right): Lieutenant G.
Bourne, RN; Stoker D.
Roberts; Able Seaman R.
Frew; Leading Seaman J.
Russell. Front row: Able
Seamen C. Boler and A.
Castle. (IWM A.28135/28134)

▶
HMS *Talent* under way in
October 1956, showing the
Mk XXIII gun on an S.2
mounting without the
shield. (Wright and Logan)

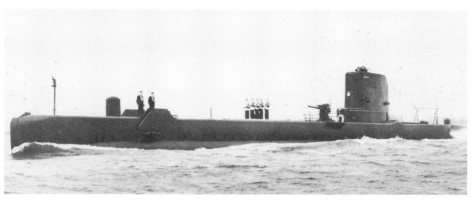

through external wells in their saddle tanks using roughly the same system as the six E-class and six L-class patrol submarine minelayers constructed during and after the First World War, although only one, *Tetrarch*, was completed with the minelaying equipment: eight mines in eight vertical mine wells set in the saddle tanks; four on each side.[24]

The mines carried were the Vickers T Mk III: a moored mine with seven Hertz horns and a 200kg charge. The rollers on the mine's two sinker guide arms engaged two vertical guide channels fitted athwartships in the wells and the mine was secured and released by a locking bolt which engaged with a plate on the mine's sinker. The locking bolts were operated by telemotor pressure or, alternatively, by hand. An extension shaft was carried to the top of the external tanks so that the locking bolt could be operated for loading purposes.[25]

The minelaying equipment gave problems from the start. Trials were carried out at Barrow on 29 December 1939 and on 10 and 11 February 1940. Vice-Admiral (Submarines) complained on 28 February 1940 that the workmanship left a lot to be desired and that *Tetrarch*'s surface speed was reduced by 1½ knots when carrying mines, and even when the chutes were unloaded surface speed would be reduced unless the mine openings were blanked off – an operation which necessitated the submarine going into dock. He concluded: '. . . assuming that the minelaying gear can be made satisfactory it is considered that the permanent sacrifice of surface speed in a large number of patrol submarines to achieve the problematical advantage of potential layers of so small a number of mines is not justified'.[27] When *Tetrarch* arrived at Portsmouth further defects in the gear became apparent and the submarine had to be docked. DTM (Director of the Torpedo and Mining Division) noted that: '. . . the gear is considered to be generally unsuitable and it is unlikely that it can be brought up to service standards without experimental work necessitating the withdrawal from service of one of the ships so fitted for at least a month with the probability of further delay for executing the modifications found necessary'.[27]

Horton agreed and decided to cut his losses. Between

16 March and 1 April 1940 the mine wells in *Tetrarch* had covers welded over the openings although it is not clear whether the minelaying gear was removed before *Tetrarch* was lost. Instructions that *Torbay* and *Talisman* were not to be fitted for minelaying and that the mine wells were to be incorporated into the main tanks' spaces were issued on 21 and 25 May 1940 respectively.[28]

But the Ts were not done with minelaying. The Admiralty had been developing its own torpedo tube laid magnetic mine; one that could be laid by any submarine. Such an idea produced some opposition with the submarine service since mines carried in this fashion lessened the number of torpedoes that could be carried. On 12 April 1940 Commander E. Gibson, Chief Staff Officer to Admiral (Submarines), commented that: '. . . the possibility of laying magnetic mines by submarine is not in fact as great an asset as before the method of laying by aircraft was developed. The carrying of mines in torpedo tubes detracts enormously from the hitting power of a submarine.'[29] Such opposition was futile. The ACNS had given orders that the mine, known as the M Mk II Mine, was to be given highest priority. Successful basin trials carried out using HMS *Tigris* in Portsmouth Dockyard were followed by further equally successful trials on 15–18 July 1940 carried out by HMS *Talisman* at Loch Long. The *Talisman* trials showed that mines could be discharged from all the six internal bow tubes at all speeds from 0 to 8 knots with the submarine on the surface or at periscope depth.[30] Discharge trials in the refitted *Triumph*, however, showed that considerable problems remained to be overcome in achieving a correct trim while minelaying and in adjusting the timing of the AIV gear. Nevertheless, on 25 September 1940 Horton wrote to Vickers, Cammell Laird, Scotts and the Royal Dockyards to order that T-class submarines be fitted with the appropriate equipment for embarking and stowing the mines although he was adamant that the work should not delay the boats' completion: thus *Thunderbolt*, *Trusty* and *Turbulent* were not fitted for minelaying. It was not until 11 March 1941 when *Torbay* carried out further trials that the problems of trimming and AIV timing were solved.

Each T class could carry eighteen of the M Mk II mines although in practice they never carried more than twelve. This meant sailing for patrol with six torpedoes short: a state of affairs not relished by many commanding officers. The general practice was to lay the mines, two mines per tube, in three salvos of four mines each using either the upper or lower pairs of tubes since the loading arrangements for the middle pair were considered unsuitable for mine stowage.[31] The mine was discharged by air pressure: the impulse throwing the mine some way ahead of the submarine before its negative buoyancy caused it to sink. The mine was fitted with a four-hour arming delay to provide a margin of safety for the submarine although there was always a certain amount of uneasiness as

the laying submarine passed over her own mines! The mine required a minimum spacing of 400 feet to prevent mutual damage or countermining. It was not a very sensitive mine and for that reason had to be laid in depths of less than ten fathoms which called for considerable navigational skill when laying submerged in restricted waters. If navigational marks were available, mines were laid by night on the surface. The first minelay conducted by a T boat was in operation S/M MLO.2: a lay of twelve mines off the Outer Mati Bank on the Sumatran coast by *Trespasser* on 14 March 1944.[33]

◄
Trenchant's conning tower seen in June 1945, showing the 20mm Oerlikon gun at the after end together with the safety rail. (IWM ABS.434)

►
Tireless, second boat from the right, in 1945, showing her twin Mk XIIA Oerlikon mounting. *Tireless* was the only boat to be so armed.

►
The 6pdr 7cwt gun, in this case mounted on an MTB, which it was intended to fit to T-class submarines to augment their gun armament. (IWM A.25164)

◄
A post-war view of an unidentified T boat, possibly *Tantivy*, showing her unique arrangement of two single 20mm Oerlikons mounted either side of the after end of the conning tower: only the starboard gun can be seen in this photograph. Note also the shield around the gun.

►
HMS *Tetrarch* alongside the coaling jetty at Blyth early in the Second World War. *Tetrarch* was the last British submarine to be completed with specially designed minelaying equipment. (National Maritime Museum)

4. Sensors and Communications

To see without being seen and to hear without being heard: such is the essence of submarine warfare. A T-class submarine used a variety of sensors in order to find her targets while remaining invulnerable to enemy attack. These sensors ranged from the human eye to sophisticated radar and ASDIC, later renamed sonar.

On the surface the role of the lookouts was vitally important: the development of radar during the Second World War did not make the lookout redundant. A submarine was most vulnerable when surfacing at dusk: enemy A/S craft could be waiting with their engines stopped for the boat to appear. In most submarines it was the practice for the commanding officer to be first on the bridge. As he unclipped the upper hatch of the conning tower he braced himself, aided by the signalman holding on to his legs, against the strong blast of foul-smelling air which would roar up the conning tower as pressure equalized in the boat. Once on the bridge, the commanding officer and signalman would each scan one side of the horizon before summoning the lookouts to the bridge.

For observation while dived a boat carried two periscopes, made of bronze so that they would not affect the magnetic compass – 'Faithful Freddie'. Careful use of these periscopes, coupled with a listening watch on the ASDIC, would ensure that the submarine was not taken unawares. When 'down' the periscopes retracted into wells sunk in the control room deck. They were raised by rams working off the telemotor system and operating wire pulleys. Where the periscope passed through the pressure hull a gland was fitted which though watertight allowed the periscope to be turned without undue force. The periscopes were 34 feet long which was a compromise length. Any shorter and the submarine would have an unacceptably low periscope depth; any higher and the periscopes would need considerable support above the top of the conning tower – thereby increasing the boat's silhouette – or the hull would have to be constructed to a more oval shape in order to accommodate a deeper periscope well. As it was, T-boat periscopes had to be supported by 'standards' rising some 10 feet above the level of the bridge.

The forward of the two periscopes was known as the 'Search' periscope and was a binocular and bifocal instrument made by Barr & Stroud. T boats used the types CK.8 and CK.9[1] which had a diameter of 9½ inches and two magnification settings: low power, or x1½, gave a field of view of 40° and was suitable for a quick all-round look at the horizon; high power, or x6, gave a field of view of only 10° which was suitable for the identification of individual objects or a detailed search of the horizon.

The other periscope, the 'Attack' periscope, was mounted aft of the Search periscope. Types used in T boats were the Barr & Stroud CH.40, CH.51 or CH.57[2] which were monocular and unifocal. The diameter of the tube was 7½ inches and the magnification was x1½, which presented the viewer with an image almost the same as that recorded by the human eye. This periscope would be used in the final stage of an attack when the small diameter of the head would make it less conspicuous than the larger search periscope.

Periscope depth was about 30 feet in a wartime T boat and some of the early boats experienced difficulty in depth-keeping while at periscope depth. *Tetrarch* (Commander R. G. Mills) was unique in that she was temporarily fitted with 40-foot perioscopes in an attempt to cure the problem. The longer periscopes were housed in the existing standards which meant that 6 feet of the periscope protruded over the tops of the standards even when the periscope was 'down'. Trials were partially successful and DNC admitted that

▲
HMS *Tuna* comes
alongside the depot ship
HMS *Forth* at Holy Loch in
August 1943. The
photograph shows the
periscope standards
which supported the two
periscopes. (IWM A.18935)

◄
Petty Officer D. G. Waldren
of *Taku* cleans the upper
window of the
submarine's 7½-inch
attack periscope using a
well-known brand of gin,
at Malta in early 1943.

▶
Lieutenant-Commander
Cecil Crouch, first and
only commanding officer
of *Thunderbolt* (ex-*Thetis*)
at the attack periscope in
the control room. Behind
him, on his left, is the
chart table. (IWM A.8461)

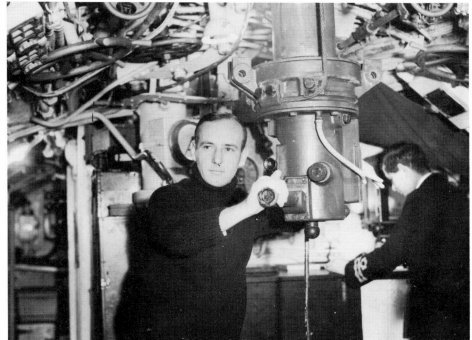

the 34-foot periscope was too short for the T class, but that it would take too long to design a new instrument.[3] The wartime Ts would have to make do with the 34-foot periscopes and other cures would have to be found for the depth-keeping problem.

The longer periscopes were eventually fitted to the T-Conversions and T-Streamlines during the post-war period. These new periscopes were 37 feet long and both were of 9½-inch diameter. The forward one was termed the attack periscope while the after periscope was now known as the 'Radar' periscope since it incorporated a Type 973 ranging radar which would give the range of a target far more accurately than the optical coincidence rangefinder.[4] The 37-foot periscopes were made of steel. This had an important effect as regards the boat's underwater speed. Boats fitted with the old bronze periscopes could do no more than 5/6 knots out of a maximum speed of 9 knots, while using the perioscope, since at the greater speeds the periscope would vibrate so much it would be unusable.

This was a considerable handicap on the boat's performance particularly those boats later fitted with a snorkel since if the CO or OOW wanted to use the periscope while making a fast dived passage using the snort he would have to reduce speed. The steel periscopes fitted in the T-Conversions and T-Streamlines were much tougher and the boat could use them while travelling at the full 9/10 knots snorkelling speed.

Periscope observations could be supplemented by information from the submarine's ASDIC equipment. The term ASDIC comes from the Allied Submarine Detection Investigation Committee set up during the First World War. After the Second World War this acronym was replaced by the American SONAR, Sound Navigation and Ranging.

T boats had two non-directional 'Tank Type' passive hydrophones, one on each side of the bows, which were capable of picking up some low-frequency sounds. The main ASDIC set fitted to T boats was the Type 129 which was used for echo-detection and

◄ The 'dome' for the 129 ASDIC set at the forward end of *Telemachus'* ballast keel. The photograph was taken in dock at Singapore in 1952. (Gus Britton)

◄ The converted *Thermopylae* alongside during a visit to London in June 1955, showing the dome for the ill-fated 171 'Four Square' set.

ranging, hydrophone listening and underwater communication (SST) at 10kHz, together with sonic listening at frequencies of between .5 to 4.5kHz.[5] Owing to the demand for ASDIC for use in surface ships, little attention was paid to the ongoing development of submarine ASDIC and as a result the Type 129 soldiered on well into the 1950s. The dome was situated at the forward end of the ballast keel with the advantage that the submarine could bottom without damaging the set. The transmitting apparatus was gyro-stabilized and could be trained either by an electric motor – early models of which were found to be rather noisy – or mechanically. The receiving apparatus together with the training and transmission control equipment were situated in a compartment opposite the wardroom on the starboard side of the boat just forward of the control room.

Designed primarily as an attack set, wartime experience showed that the 129 had excellent hydrophone capabilities and a second listening position was established in the fore ends by the bulkhead between the tube space and the torpedo stowage compartment far from the noise and vibration produced by the diesels. The list of variations to the 129 is almost endless and included an omni-directional hydrophone, the Type 129K, tested in HMS *Thrasher*, and a short pulse variant for detecting mines at ranges from 700 to 1,500 yards, which was first fitted to HMS *Triad*.[6] However, the 129 had one drawback: its position at the forward end of the ballast keel meant that there was a blind arc of about 20° on each side of the stern bearing. In 1943 a Type 138 listening set with manual training was fitted to all new construction T boats, and retro-fitted to the others, in a position on the after casing between 9 and 10 tubes. This position meant that the set had to be accommodated in the engine room and considerable problems were encountered in doing so.[7]

The 129/138 combination survived into the post-war era but with the advent of the concept of the 'Fighter' submarine, (*see* Chapter 9) it was clear that something

▶ **The Streamlined *Token* under way in 1961, showing the two 168 set domes on the casing, one forward and one aft, fitted to give a passive ranging capacity.**

a little more sophisticated was required. To begin with the 138 passive set was given an active capability and renamed 138F. This set was now capable of hydrophone listening at 14kHz, echo-ranging and SST facilities on the same frequency and sonic listening at between .5 to 4.5kHz.[8] As another interim measure the 129/138 combination was upgraded and renamed 169/168.

These, however, were but interim measures. The growing emphasis on the offensive role of the submarine, particularly against transiting Soviet submarines, meant that a new set was required: one that would provide a 'three-dimensional' picture. The great hope of the post-war period was the Type 171 or 'Four Square' set which was the submarine variant of the Type 170 set fitted in destroyers and frigates. 'Four Square' would give accurate hydrophone bearings at 20kHz, echo-ranging at 20kHz with target location above or below the submarine's depth.[9] The set would also provide mine detection in both the horizontal and the vertical planes. The set was intended for introduction into the T-Conversions and would be installed in an inverted dome at the bow. But by the time *Taciturn*, the first of the conversions, commissioned in March 1951, 'Four Square' was by no means ready. In the meantime the installation of 138F/168 on the forward casing was to proceed in such a manner that 'Four Square' could easily be fitted once it became available.

'Four Square' was to be combined with 718, a 'split beam', low-frequency precision tracking hydrophone similar to the American JT set which had been experimentally fitted in *Truncheon*. This combination was first fitted in *Thermopylae*, the fourth of the T-Conversions. The large dome on *Thermopylae*'s bow was the source of much interested Press speculation when she commissioned. Alas, the set did not perform well. It was quickly apparent that 'Four Square's' depth determination abilities were inadequate. In trials against HMS *Ambush* off Gibraltar, *Thermopylae*'s 171 indicated that *Ambush* was 500 feet above her instead of the reverse. It was clear that the problem could be remedied only by fitting of extensive computer support which could not be accommodated within a submarine's hull so 'Four Square' was quietly dropped.[10]

Thus the Ts were forced back on the 169/168 combination which was to remain the standard fit until the end of the 1950s. In an effort to upgrade the equipment some boats began carrying one or more domes for the 168 set, widely spaced to give improved bearing accuracy and a better passive ranging capability: indeed this arrangement became almost standard in the five T-Streamlines. Twin 168 were also fitted in some of the eight T-Conversions until 1958 when the 187 set appeared. 187 was little more than a 718 hydrophone set, but with a limited active capacity. It consisted of a 5-foot wide transducer rotated mechanically within a large streamlined dome on the bow.[11] All eight T-Conversions (except *Totem* which had to wait until she was sold to the Israelis before receiving hers) were subsequently fitted with the large dome, but it is not clear as to how many were actually fitted with the 187 set.

Type 187 was used in conjunction with the 719 hydrophone set which was mounted in a small bulge on the after end of the fin. The 187/719 combination did not provide the T-Conversions with an adequate long-range detection capability. Captain John Coote, who commanded *Totem* in her first commission, recalled that '. . . *Totem* had no long-range sonar detection capability. If the opposition had obliged by passing within range, then fine, but we didn't expect to be able to detect a snorkelling submarine at more than about five miles in good conditions . . . not far in terms of what followed.[12]

Contrary to some reports neither the T-Conversions nor the T-Streamlines were fitted with the 186 hydrophone or 'Knout'. This long-range detection system, developed from German GHG equipment, consisted of a pair of arrays on each side of the submarine. However, *Thule* in her unconverted 'gunboat' state had carried out trials of the equipment, and *Tireless* was also experimentally fitted with it after her streamlining.

◀
HMS *Thule* out of Portsmouth in January 1955, showing the two hydrophone arrays forward and aft of her conning tower during trials of the 186 'Knout' passive hydrophone. The prominent twin domes on her casing are possibly a twin 168 set. (Wright and Logan)

▶
Tiptoe's conning tower at Barrow in June 1944, showing the paraboloid aerial for the SJ set on its non-elevating mast. (IWM FL.4028)

▶
HMS *Totem*'s bridge in 1945, showing the X-shaped aerial with the four dipoles for the 291W radar set. Note also the totem-pole emblem fixed to the front of the bridge. Legend had it that if the submarine put to sea without the pole onboard she would be lost. (Gus Britton)

Radar was in its infancy when the T boats were being designed and no provision was made for this equipment: a suitable submarine set did not exist. Radar would enable a submarine to locate targets that might be missed due to darkness or poor visibility, and provided warning of air attack or enemy A/S measures. The first submarine set was the 291 P-band (214m/cs) which could also be fitted in destroyers and other small craft. The submarine variant was 291W for which the aerial was designed to remain watertight under pressure. Detection ranges with the boat at periscope depth, with the mast at 4 feet above the water, and with the boat on the surface with the aerial 30 feet above the water were:

Target	Aerial at 4 feet	Aerial at 30 feet
Battleship	2nm	5.5nm
Destroyer	1nm	3.5nm
Submarine	0.5nm	2nm
Aircraft:		
at 10,000 feet	17nm	30nm
at 5,000 feet	12nm	25nm
at 1,000 feet	4nm	15nm[13]

The installation was simple and could be carried out in as little as seven days. The aerial consisted of four dipoles mounted on an X-shaped frame fitted at the after end of the bridge in place of the W/T mast. The aerial was mounted on a telescopic APT mast and connected to the set by a coaxial cable and was rotated manually by the operator using a wheel through a series of universal couplings. Deterioration of these couplings and their bearings made considerable maintenance necessary. Interlocks were fitted in order to prevent damage to the aerial by lowering the mast with the aerial in any but the fore-and-aft stowing position or by training the mast before the aerial was clear of the jumping wire.[14]

This set was run off the boat's DC supply, which drove a very noisy rotary converter. The equipment was fitted in the already crowded W/T office and the heat generated by the set would raise the temperature to well over 110°F. Both *Taurus* (Lieutenant-Commander M. R. Wingfield) and *Tactician* (Lieutenant-Commander A. F. Collett) reported that soldered connections melted as a result of the heat in the W/T office.[15] Boats going to the Far East were fitted with two transmitters and used them alternately for periods of 30 minutes at a time. Presentation was via an A tube display in the W/T office. One of the problems with the set was that its long wavelength gave it poor definition against surface targets; however, it proved to be relatively effective against aircraft. Initial reaction to the fitting of radar in submarines was not enthusiastic. 'The Mk 1 Eyeball is more effective than your radar stuff and it takes up less room', was the comment of one T-boat commander when faced with the prospect of the installation of 291.[16]

Tuna (Lieutenant-Commander R. P. Raikes) was the first T boat to be fitted with 291W during a refit at Devonport in 1942. The set was greeted with some enthusiasm which faded rapidly once it was used at sea: '. . . on the first patrol we used it we got so frightened we switched it off because every night we were apparently being attacked from all sides.'[17] One of the deficiencies of 291W was its inability to distinguish between a rain squall and an approaching aircraft, a problem that was to be exasperating for OOWs and lookouts. The principal use for 291W was air warning when the boat was on the surface at night while charging batteries. When dived the set could be used to give an all-round sweep for prowling aircraft/ASW forces before surfacing. *Thorough* (Lieutenant A.

G. Chandler) reported that the set was also useful for navigation at ranges of 15,000 yards and on one occasion got a rough fix on a mountain at an astonishing range of 55 miles![18]

By July 1943 Admiral (Submarines) was exhorting his commanders to become 'radar-minded', particularly regarding the offensive use of radar. One example cited of such use of the 291W was by *Tactician* (Lieutenant-Commander A. F. Collett). Captain (S)8 reported that on the evening of 5 May 1943 while on patrol off the east coast of Corsica: '. . . whilst withdrawing for the night a large laden three-masted schooner [the 385-ton *Pia*] was sighted. At 1911 *Tactician* surfaced and destroyed it by gunfire. Radar was employed for ranging in this very successful shoot.'[19]

In the Far East, however, the use of radar for fire control purposes was not always practicable. *Thorough* (Lieutenant A. G. Chandler) reported that used close inshore in support of gun action the set gave off too many back echoes and clutter to make spotting by radar reliable. Moreover there were growing fears that the Japanese had a metric band receiver and could home in on transmissions.[20] Improvements to the 291W included power training, but by the middle of 1943 it was apparent that submarines required an enhanced surface warning capability not provided by the existing equipment. The requirement for a surface set was issued in June 1943, but work proceeded slowly since

◀
Tapir under way on completion in December 1944, showing the seaguard aerial for the 267W set at the forward end of the periscope standards. The airguard aerial, not visible in the photograph, remains at the after end of the conning tower.

◀
Tactician diving while serving with the Far East Fleet in the early 1950s, and showing the arrangement of the 267MW radar with the X-shaped airguard aerial forward of the periscope standards and the 'cheese' seaguard aerial at the after end. (IWM A.32248)

▶
The PPI and associated displays for a 267 set.

the RAF had priority on radar development. As an interim measure three SJ set conversion kits were acquired from the USA.

SJ was a submarine S-band (1,500–5,000MHz) surface search set which was decidedly superior to anything produced in Britain and was already being used to deadly effect by US submarines operating in the Pacific. It gave detection ranges of 12nm on a battleship and 8nm on a destroyer.[21] Two T-class submarines, *Tiptoe* and *Trump*, were fitted with this set while the third was retained as an instructional model and eventually fitted to *Truculent* after her return from the Far East.

The characteristic 30-inch paraboloid aerial was mounted on an extension to the periscope standards and thus was incapable of anything but rotary motion. It was designed to rotate at 6rpm, but experience in *Tiptoe* (Lieutenant-Commander R. L. Jay) was that the set performed better at 4rpm due to vibration in the mast. *Tiptoe* reported achieving excellent results with SJ in her first patrol from Fremantle (6 May–17 June 1945) in which a 982-ton freighter was torpedoed. Likewise *Trump*'s (Lieutenant A. A. Catlow) first patrol in the SW Pacific area was described as 'active and aggressive'[22] in which four ships were sunk, an armed trawler damaged and a bridge shelled. *Trump* and *Tiptoe* later operated together within five miles of each other. On 3 August *Trump*, using her SJ, found a convoy of four large ships one of which was a tanker escorted by

a destroyer, and two patrol vessels with air cover. *Trump* got the first attack in and sank one ship. *Tiptoe* was four miles to the northward and received *Trump*'s enemy report and in extremely shallow water, Jay fired at the leading ship, having given *Tiptoe* a 'bows up' angle to prevent the torpedoes hitting the bottom, and scored one hit. On firing, she was almost aground with 40 feet showing on the depth gauge. Captain Ben Bryant, Captain (S)4, remarked that this attack was 'equal in courage and determination, as well as skill, to any submarine attack of the war'.[23]

SJ could also be used for communications purposes via a sideband, but the extempore nature of its installation in *Tiptoe* and *Trump* meant that the boats were not able to obtain the same performance with their SJs as the American boats which had the aerial on an elevating mast and could use the equipment for torpedo attacks while dived. *Truculent*'s post-war SJ installation was a little different. The aerial was mounted at the forward end of the standards which allowed her to carry 291W, giving her an enhanced air warning capability.

Development of what was coyly described as the 'ideal set' in terms of a surface warning set was some way off, so as an interim measure the 267W set was introduced for surface warning in submarines. However, in the best traditions of British defence procurement, 267 would continue in a number of variants as an 'interim measure' until the early 1960s. Type 267W was a dual frequency (P- and X-band) set combining the P-band airguard facilities of 291W with an X-band surface search capability. Both aerials were power rotated: the P-band dipoles remained in the after mounting, but a second 'cheese' aerial for the X-band element was to be fitted immediately forward of the periscope standards on a non-elevating APS mast approximately 2 feet above the periscope standards. In this position should the CO wish to use the set while dived he would have to run with his periscope standards almost awash. Presentation was by a master PPI in the W/T office with a second slave PPI in the control room above the chart table. On trials the following ranges were obtained:

Battleship	19nm
Destroyer	13nm (max.) 11nm (reliable)
U-class S/M	6nm[24]

The range accuracy was 25 yards and bearing accuracy was $+-\frac{1}{2}°$. The laboratory model was first fitted in *Tuna*, but the trials were a complete disaster. The set went back to the laboratory for modification before being refitted in *Tuna* for a more successful series of trials before being fitted in *Turpin* (Lieutenant-Commander J. S. Stevens) completing at Chatham and *Tapir* (Lieutenant-Commander J. C. Y. Roxburgh) completing at Barrow. During trials of the equipment *Tapir*'s commanding officer, now Vice-Admiral Sir John Roxburgh, recalled that the new 267 set gave: '. . . a very fine picture. It was marvellous going round Scotland

and seeing the whole coastline. It gave the most wonderful picture compared with the rather murky picture obtained from the airguard set.'[25]

In April 1945 *Tapir* and *Turpin* sailed for patrol off the Norwegian coast in adjoining billets and in doing so gave 267W its first operational trial. As Admiral Roxburgh later remembered:

'On the first night, 6 April, in my billet we picked up on our ASDICs an enemy submarine which we proceeded to stalk. We then heard it surface so I immediately broke surface to get my 267 radar on it. I got a lovely blip of it and I tracked it very quickly with my standards sticking up about 5–6 feet whilst I got a picture. He was going away at speed so I surfaced to chase him and was overtaking him, but he was about to leave my area and into Stevens', [Lieutenant-Commander J. S. Stevens in *Turpin*] who was patrolling next door. I could see I wasn't going to catch up with him so I got ready to send an enemy report when suddenly to my astonishment, I got the correct challenge from the other side immediately followed by "Don't shoot, Steve here!"'[26]

Turpin had found herself out of position and had come to the surface to return at speed to her own area. Her 267W radar operator reported a contact astern and speed was reduced to assist development of a range and bearing plot. It was only when *Turpin*'s operator reported mutual interference that Stevens realized that his assailant could only be *Tapir*.[27] *Turpin* had a lucky escape for had *Tapir* come within range Roxburgh would have undoubtedly fired. Six days later Roxburgh dispatched *U486* (Oberleutnant zur See Gerhardt Meyer) in the same area.

The 267W variant was also fitted in *Tireless*, *Token*, *Truncheon* and the Dutch *Tijgerhaai*, but was quickly replaced by 267MW in which the aerials were rearranged: the first Ts to be so fitted were *Tabard*, *Teredo* and *Thermopylae*, and it was retro-fitted to all the boats selected for inclusion in the post-war fleet. In 267MW the airguard aerial was now mounted forward of the periscope standards on a telescopic APT mast and the seaguard aerial on a periscopic ANF mast in the position aft of the standards formerly occupied by the airguard aerial.[28] This was a greatly improved arrange-

◀
Lieutenant D. S. Schrijvershof, commanding officer of Hr Ms *Tijgerhaai*, on the bridge in October 1958. The photograph gives an excellent view of the 267MW seaguard aerial on the periscopic ANF mast. (Royal Netherlands Navy)

▲
Lieutenant E. F. Balston, leaning over the forward edge of the bridge, brings

▲
Tribune alongside HMS *Forth*. The photograph shows the W/T mast in the raised position and doubling as a mast from which are flying the signal flags for *Tribune*'s pennant number and an additional white ensign as insurance against the over-zealous attentions of the RAF.

▲
Tribune's wireless office showing the Type 55 transmitter and associated equipment. With the addition of radar equipment this compartment rapidly became extremely crowded. (IWM A.10905)

▼
Taciturn leaving Portsmouth in October 1960, showing her radar mast in the raised position and topped with the aerial for the 1000 series navigational radar which replaced the 267PW set. The photograph also shows the conspicuous bow dome for the 187 sonar set. The bulge in the after edge of the fin is for the 719 hydrophone.

ment, since the boat could use the seaguard aerial while at periscope depth instead of having to trundle along with her standards awash. 267MW also gave improved detection ranges. Using the set while dived, aircraft at 17 miles at 10,000 feet, 12 miles at 3,000 feet or 4 miles at 1,000 feet could be detected. Battleships were detected at 7.5 miles, destroyers at 5.5 miles and a submarine at 3.5 miles.[29] When in the down position, the airguard aerial was housed in the bridge space, but the seaguard aerial required another 'well' to be sunk in the control room deck to accommodate the fully retracting mast which meant that there had to be a

certain rearrangement of tank spaces beneath the control room.

267PW was an upgraded variant of the set fitted in the T-Conversions and the T-Streamlines on separate periscopic masts within the 'fin' structure. However such an extensive radar suite was incompatible with their new role as submarine-hunters. There were few circumstances in which radar could be employed in a tactical situation to provide information which was not provided by the improved ASDIC. Moreover, use of the radar could be a liability, for although the submarine's radar mast, if raised while the boat was at periscope

▶
The streamlined *Tireless* under way on 24 September 1952, showing, aft of the conning tower, the frame which supported the HF transmitting aerial. (IWM FL.3563)

depth, would be within the microwave 'duct' formed by vapour over the water and therefore indetectable to other radars, the emissions from the set would indicate the boat's position to any escort. ESM (Electronic Support Measures – the passive detection of radar emissions) were gradually viewed as more important for detecting the opposition's use of radar without giving away the boat's position.

T-Conversions carried X-band radar intercept gear on the W/T mast. *Totem* (Commander J. Coote) also incorporated an S-band intercept gear into her 'radar' periscope which was fitted by the ship's staff and

which gave immunity against the AN/APS20 airborne radar and shipborne S-band search radars. It was an unauthorized modification, not fitted to any other T-Conversion, and consisted of a snout containing a 7-inch S-band horn which was brazed on to the periscope below the upper window. It was wired down to a headset worn by the OOW when on periscope watch.[30]

Taciturn was fitted with what appeared to be an aerial for a Type-1000 series combined airguard/seaguard set, but it is not known how many of the other Conversions received this equipment: photographs showing their radar masts raised are rare.

As well as radar, T boats were also fitted with the 253MW Mk III IFF (Identification, Friend or Foe) system which automatically identified the submarine as 'friendly' to Allied aircraft equipped with ASV (air to surface vessel) radar. 253MW consisted of a responder operating with the 267MW set which allowed both signals to be displayed on the same PPI. The ASH-type aerial was mounted on the periscope standards.[31] IFF was not fitted to the Conversions or Streamlines as the Admiralty were unsure of future IFF policy. Details of the fitting of any subsequent IFF equipment are unknown.

Submarine communications were, and are, a mostly one way business. The boat has to be able to receive signals from home, but no commander would give his position away by transmitting unless absolutely essential. Signals were passed to the boat from ashore by VLF which allowed the boat to listen at periscope depth virtually anywhere in the world. The signals were broadcast and repeated at regular times, roughly every four hours, from the transmitter at Rugby. It was therefore mandatory for the boat to 'read' the routine transmission twice a day. The duty telegraphist had to warn the CO/OOW before each transmission from Rugby so that the boat could be turned on to the correct course. Such calls could often come at highly inconvenient moments! However, a constant watch had to be kept for important signals which could be sent at any time. For VLF reception a T boat had a long wire aerial strung out along the length of the forward jumping wire. At 45 feet it was theoretically possible to receive signals from Rugby at distances of up to 2,000 miles provided the boat was 'pointed' so that the bow or stern was within 40° of the transmitter. At periscope depth 'pointing' was only required to within 60° of the transmitter.[32] This method of signal reception greatly affected operations. The optimum course for reception might drain the battery if it proved difficult to keep a steady depth. Moreover, should the boat inadvertently go deep, part of the message would be missed.

Early T boats were fitted with a telescopic three-throw mast at the after end of the conning tower to support the HF transmitting aerial. Early Group One T boats often had spurs attached to the aerial mast which were used as yardarms for hoisting signal flags. The mast was an extremely cumbersome arrangement and did not last long before being removed to make way for

the 20mm Oerlikon platform. The HF aerial was then adapted to consist of two 30-foot lengths of insulated cable running forward and aft of the periscope standards, to which it was secured by wooden blocks, and secured to the jumping wire at each end by insulated metal fittings.[33] The periscope standards also supported a small VHF aerial. The boat had to surface to transmit: a major disadvantage since she could be found by enemy Direction Finding (DF). As if the dangers of transmitting on the surface were not enough, the system was not always reliable. Commander A. R. Hezlet in *Trenchant* recalled trying to send to Trincomalee from the Malacca Strait and being answered by Halifax, Nova Scotia! His was not the only such experience.[34]

Inside the boat, the W/T office on the port side aft of the control room housed the receiving and transmitting equipment. It was a hot and crowded compartment – it contained the Type 54 or 55 transmitter,[35] two receiver outfits, CDC and CDF, and the DF equipment – at the best of times, but became even more so when the radar equipment and operators were squeezed in.

A FM4 or FM11 DF coil was also carried on the after casing between 9 and 10 tubes although in some Group Two boats not armed with an Oerlikon it was mounted at the after end of the conning tower. There was some doubt as to whether DF should be carried, but it was pointed out that it would be useful in the Far East for pin-pointing the movements of the Japanese Fleet. Alas, performance of this equipment did not match expectations: it was apt to give misleading results.[36]

These arrangements remained fairly standard in the unconverted Ts although it was possible to fit a VHF aerial to the seaguard radar mast to provide a transmitting capability while the boat was at periscope depth. In the T-Conversions, however, the aerial layout was rearranged. The HF and VHF aerials were carried on a periscopic mast within the fin which could be raised to provide a transmitting capability while dived. The fin also contained the VLF loop aerial supported by the two periscopes together with a hand-worked HF aerial for emergency use.[37] However, the loop was replaced by outfit ALF which consisted of two coils placed in the fin: one aligned fore and aft, the other athwartships. Trials in *Taciturn* showed that ALF gave the same results as those obtained with the loop aerial with the added advantage that the submarine did not need to be 'pointed' during reception of signal traffic to the same extent.

Arrangements in the five Streamlines were roughly similar. The VLF loop was fitted in the fin and subsequently replaced by the ALF aerial. However, the Streamlines' conversion did not run to the inclusion of a separate W/T mast so the HF transmitting aerial was strung aft of the conning tower and secured to a prominent frame on the after casing. The Conversions and Streamlines also received modified W/T equipment. The CDC and CDF receivers were removed and replaced by two CDW and CDY-type receivers. The DF equipment was also removed.[38] However, despite the electronic revolution in naval warfare in the late twentieth century, the operational problems associated with submarine communications which HMS *Tiptoe*, last of the operationally running T Conversions, faced in 1968 at the end of her days were exactly the same as those faced by HMS *Triton* nearly thirty years earlier.

5. Life Below

The interior of a T-class submarine was a complicated maze of machinery. Although the 53 boats differed substantially in their external appearance, their interior layout was almost identical. The pressure hull was circular in section and was divided into six sections by five watertight bulkheads.

The pressure hull was 16 feet in diameter. The top of the pressure hull was pierced with six openings; from forward to aft: the forward escape hatch, the torpedo loading hatch, the gun tower, conning tower, engine room hatch and after escape hatch. In addition there was the 'soft patch' in the pressure hull over the engine room which could be lifted in order to install or remove large pieces of machinery.

Access into the submarine was usually via the torpedo-loading hatch which led down into the torpedo-stowage compartment or fore-ends. At the foreward end of this compartment through the first watertight bulkhead was the Tube Space, containing the six internal torpedo tubes. Aft of the Torpedo Stowage Compartment and through the second watertight bulkhead were the accommodation areas for all the crew except the commanding officer and the stokers. The various messes led off a passageway which ran down the starboard side of the boat. At the end of this passageway was the third watertight bulkhead through which was the control room, the heart of the submarine, and the commanding officer's cabin.

The interior of the control room was dominated by the two periscopes. Along the port side were the hydroplane operators' positions while the helmsman sat facing forward at the forward end. The control room contained the attack instruments, the chart table, gyro-compass, ASDIC listening position and 'Blowing Panel'. At the after end of the control room were the galley on the starboard side, and W/T office on the port side. From the control room a ladder lead up through the conning tower to the bridge. In the early boats of the class the bridge was comprehensively fitted out with a chart table, engine room telegraphs and a steering position. Communication with the control room was via voicepipes. The two standards, on which were fitted positions for the lookouts to stand, projected above the bridge. Access to the gun position, which was below and in front of the bridge, was via the gun tower which led down into the control room. Further aft and through the fourth watertight bulkhead were the engine and motor rooms containing the two diesels and two electric motors. Through the fifth and last watertight bulkhead was the stokers' messdeck and the steering machinery space.

But a T boat was more than a mass of machinery: it was 'home' for 53 officers and men. Accommodation and comfort had never been accorded a high priority in British warship design, and submarines, by their very nature, were uncomfortable in the extreme. There was, perhaps, an attitude of 'hardship for hardship's sake' among senior naval officers when considering the arrangement of accommodation spaces, and a belief that improvements in habitability would only detract from efficiency. In the early submarines the crew had to make the best of things by sleeping on the deck or in the few areas not occupied by machinery. With the design of the T class, the Admiralty made a determined attempt to provide an enhanced standard of accommodation, Admiral (Submarines) noting in

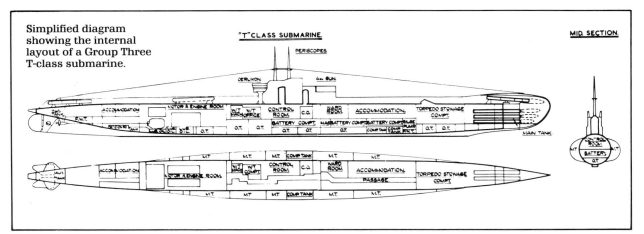

Simplified diagram showing the internal layout of a Group Three T-class submarine.

1934 that: '. . . machinery which is run continually or which is likely to leak oil should be kept out of living spaces. Messes in the torpedo working space cannot be accepted in this design.'[1] The original scheme of complement was 48 officers and men, but this was increased to 53 during the design process. No two T-class submarines ever had the same complement, but a representative crew for a Group One boat would be:

Description	Number borne
Executive Department:	
Lieutenant-Commander: in command	1
Lieutenant	2
Sub-Lieutenant	1
TGM	1
Petty Officers	3
Leading Seamen	3
Able Seamen	9
Leading Signalman	1
CPO Telegraphist	1
PO Telegraphist	1
Leading Telegraphist	1
Telegraphists	1
Engineering Department:	
Engineer Officer	1
CERA	1
ERAs	4
CPO Stoker	1
Stoker PO	1
Leading Stokers	4
Stokers	11
Others:	
Electrical Artificer	1
Leading Cook	1
Leading Steward	1*
Officers' cook	1

*Who was to be Chinese if the boat were serving in the Far East.[2]

In July 1942 Lieutenant A. J. Priest, an official Admiralty photographer, visited HMS *Tribune*, or 'Tribs' as she was affectionately known. He recorded her interior as far as was allowed by security regulations and his are the majority of illustrations used in this chapter. They are an excellent record of the interior of the pre-war T boat. Constructed in peacetime by a private yard, Scotts, *Tribune* was fitted with many of the little 'extras' in the way of finish that would not be possible had the boat been built in a Royal Dockyard or under wartime conditions.

Most of the crew lived between the torpedo stowage compartment and the control room, only the stokers lived aft. Seventeen of the seamen lived in an open messdeck which was described thus: 'The majority of the bunks were in the mess around the tables where the top bunks were lowered to form the backs of the seats which also served as bunks. A very nice arrangement when nobody wanted to sleep but in a three-watch routine on a normal patrol there was always a conflict between the sleepers and those who wanted to read, play cards or uckers, etc.'[3] Bunks were also fitted down the outboard side of a passageway which ran down the starboard side of the boat off which lay other messdecks. Walking aft down this passageway one passed the separate messes for the eight CPOs and POs and five ERAs before coming to the wardroom just forward of the watertight bulkhead leading through into the control room. Four officers lived in the wardroom, the First Lieutenant, Torpedo Officer, Navigator and Engineer Officer. Although the wardroom was furnished somewhat more comfortably than the other messes, it was no less cramped.

In the T boats the commanding officer had a cabin, in reality little more than a plated-off corner of the

◀
Tribune's fore-ends in 1942. This compartment had a multiplicity of roles: note the reload torpedoes; the cornflakes stowed on the torpedo loading rails overhead and the hideous disorder of kitbags, hammocks and other stores. (IWM A.10909)

▶
Bunks lining the outboard side of the passageway running down *Tribune*'s starboard side. (IWM A.10906)

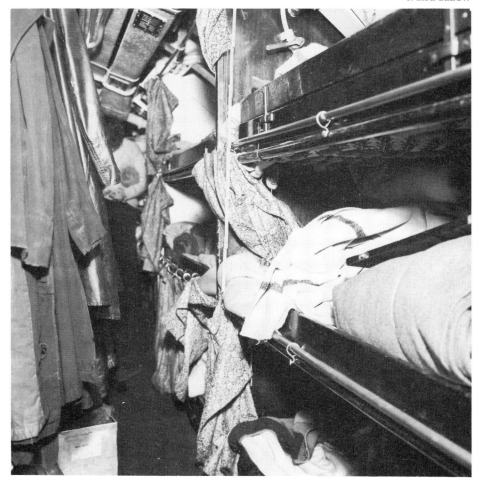

▶
A convivial scene during the daily issue of rum in *Tuna*'s forward messdeck which housed seventeen seamen. (IWM A.18936)

control room on the port forward side. Possession of a cabin was a considerable blessing for the CO, '. . . it was a great thing to have a cabin as a Captain it was somewhere I could just "be" on my own' recalled one CO.[4] But although the possession of a cabin conferred a degree of privacy, the CO was always aware of what was going on outside. Lieutenant-Commander R. B. Foster recalled an example of this in *Turbulent* (Commander J. W. 'Tubby' Linton) when the submarine was lying dived off Dubrovnik, and brought back pleasant memories for one member of the control room watch:

'As soon as he knew where we were he kept regaling the control room with his sexual experiences during a pre-war Mediterranean fleet visit to Dubrovnik. He apparently had his first but certainly his best, experience with a "lovely bit of stuff" and we had a blow-by-blow account of the whole evening and it looked as if it would go on for the whole watch. After a quarter of an hour Tubby came out of his cabin and said "No 1, for God's sake put the periscope up, train it on the town and give X two ten-second looks at the scene of his greatest triumph. If you don't we shall probably have a seizure or a sexual explosion on our hands. The watch can then have some peace and I can get some sleep."[5]

Given that habitability came fairly low down on the list of priorities in British submarine design, those who served in T boats had generally favourable views about their accommodation. Cramped conditions were accepted as part of a submariner's lot: a T-boat man simply had to visit his 'oppo' in an S or U/V class submarine to realize how well off he was! Even in harbour with the facilities of a depot ship or shore establishment available, many T-boat men preferred to remain in the boat,[6] although this may have been a result of the close sense of camaraderie among submarine crews.

Although the complement rose to 53 during the design stage, the number of bunks remained at 48 and it was necessary to make alternative arrangements for the remainder. 'Hot-bunking' – simply described as one man moving into a bunk still warm from the previous occupant – was one solution, but was clearly unacceptable in the tropics and it became necessary to embark hammocks to be slung in the torpedo stowage compartment, or fore-ends, for the additional ratings. During the war still more men were required to work the extra guns, torpedo tubes, ASDIC and radar sets, which brought the complement up to 61. Accommodation was provided in the form of collapsible berths fitted in the fore-ends, so designed that they did not interfere with the handling of the torpedoes. Although some members of the crew would always be on watch, the lack of bunks was a perennial complaint. Messing in the fore-ends was considered unsatisfactory since men had to: '. . . compete with the bread and fresh vegetables which

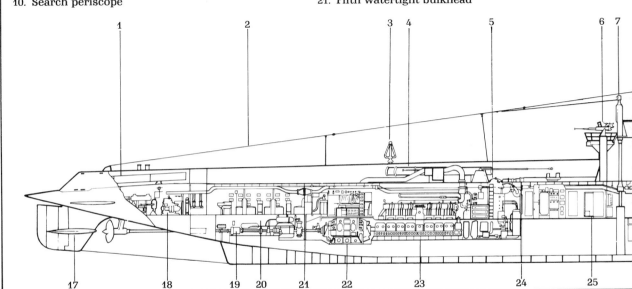

Sectional drawing of a T-Class submarine
1. External torpedo-tube
2. Jumping-wire
3. DF Coil
4. External torpedo-tube
5. Engine-room hatch
6. 20mm Oerlikon gun
7. Type 267 Seaguard radar
8. Attack periscope
9. Upper and lower conning-tower hatches
10. Search periscope
11. Type 291 Airguard radar
12. Upper and lower gun-tower hatches
13. 4in gun
14. Jumping-wire
15. Torpedo loading hatch
16. External torpedo-tube
17. After hydroplanes
18. Steering compartment
19. Auxiliary machinery
20. Stoker mechanics' mess
21. Fifth watertight bulkhead

deteriorated rapidly, producing unsavoury odours. When there was a need for torpedo maintenance everything had to be cleared out of the way to the great annoyance of all.'[7]

At the after end of the control room, but before the engine room were the W/T office on the port side and the galley on the starboard side. The galley was fitted with a cooking range comprising three ovens, four hot plates, one grill, a four-gallon water boiler and a hot cupboard. Stores were stowed in a compartment below the forward end of the control room between Nos. 2 and 3 batteries, but there was nowhere near the space required to stow everything. Consequently supplies were stowed throughout the boat in the most unlikely places. The fore-ends was the usual place, but R. G. Jones remembers the escape chambers in *Tuna* coming in handy as a potato store.[8] For long patrols in the Far East, tinned food was often stowed so as to form a false deck which was gradually 'removed' as the patrol went on. Stowage of all supplies and stores in a fashion that did not upset the trim was the Coxswain's responsibility. Keeping food fresh, particularly in the tropics, was a problem. Two cold cupboards of 40 and 10 cubic feet respectively were fitted as standard and these were supplemented with a 5-cubic-foot refrigerator together with a 20-cubic-foot cold cupboard.[9]

Food in a wartime T boat was adequate but hardly imaginative, despite Horton's insistence that there be no rationing in submarines, though in comparison with the civilian population submariners lived like kings. Much depended on the chef and his was not an easy task. In the heat of the Mediterranean or Malacca Straits the atmosphere in the tiny galley, with the boat plunging and rolling and with the temperature perhaps over 100°F, was fairly unpleasant to say the least!

In Home Waters and the Mediterranean, tinned and dried provisions made up the bulk of provisions since fresh food deteriorated rapidly inside the boat and had to be consumed quickly. However, those T boats that were based in Fremantle in Australia and had access to the vast and unrationed Australian food supply, went to sea with rations that would have made a British housewife struggling with her 'points' and 'coupons' marvel. When *Tantalus* (Lieutenant-Commander H. S. Mackenzie) sailed on her second SW Pacific patrol (3 January–26 February 1945) she was carrying no less than the following fresh provisions: 3,256lb potatoes, 600lb other vegetables, 400lb butter, 450lb beef, 150lb mutton, 100lb pork, 16 cases of fruit, 210 dozen eggs, 107lb poultry, 400lb bread, 1,940lb flour and 12lb butter as well as a considerable amount of tinned and dried stores![10]

Submarine operations would not be allowed to interfere with the hallowed ritual of the daily 'tot'. Senior

22. Main motors and switch gear
23. Diesel engines
24. Fourth watertight bulkhead
25. Radar and W/T offices
26. Control room
27. No. 3 battery
28. Commanding officer's cabin
29. Store
30. Third watertight bulkhead
31. Magazine
32. Ward room

33. No. 2 battery
34. Engine room artificers' mess
35. Petty Officers' mess
36. No. 1 battery
37. Seamen's mess
38. Auxiliary machinery
39. Second watertight bulkhead
40. Torpedo stowage compartment
41. First watertight bulkhead
42. Type 129 ASDIC
43. Torpedo-tube compartment

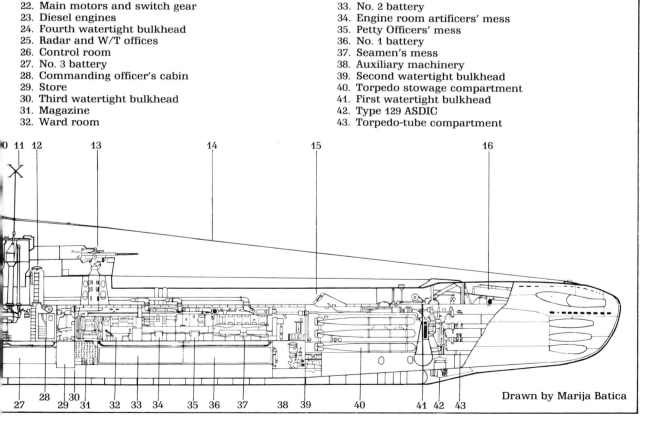

Drawn by Marija Batica

rates received their rum neat and junior rates were supposed to have their diluted, but it would appear that, contrary to general naval practice, rum was issued neat to junior rates in submarines. The rum was supposed to be consumed immediately but ratings sufficiently removed from the control room, or under the eye of an officer or PO, would save their ration in a 'blitz bottle' for consolation during a depth-charge hammering.

All rubbish or 'gash' was ditched over the side, tins and other containers being punctured to ensure that they sank. At night the order 'Ditch gash!' was given. 'Gash', of all kinds, was hauled up the conning tower in buckets on the end of a greasy rope. In bad weather the bucket might hit an obstruction in the tower and deposit its contents on the head of an ungrateful recipient.

Heads (WCs) and washing facilities were situated forward for the seamen, amidships for the officers, aft of the control room for the POs and right aft for the stokers. The after heads were situated beneath the motor room between the propeller shafts and reached via a hatch in the motor room deck. The heads were of the compressed air variety which could only be blown by permission of the OOW when dived so that the

discharge would not reveal the boat's position. Eleven separate operations were required otherwise the user would experience the phenomenon of 'getting his own back'. The result of such an accident in a 3-foot square compartment was highly unpleasant. The sound of a 'blow back' was very distinctive and would usually be greeted with a cheer from the man's unsympathetic messmates. During war patrols when the boat had to remain dived for long periods it was not always possible for the heads to be blown so Elsan chemical lavatories were supplied. Early T boats had an additional WC in the conning tower for the watchkeepers, but it was very vulnerable to depth-charge damage and after *Truant*'s was smashed in the counter-attack following her sinking of *Karlsruhe* this fitting was removed. Despite all the experience gained in the First World War, sanitary fittings were initially made of porcelain, but after numerous boats reported their propensity to shatter when a depth-charge went off, metal fittings were substituted.

T boats had at least the impression of greater space due to the fact that the four Leading Stokers and eleven Stokers lived aft of the motor room: '. . . the stokers liked being on their own back aft. What tricks they got up to back there, God only knows',[11] recalled one CO.

View looking forward in *Telemachus'* fore-ends in a carefully posed scene showing a torpedo being loaded into No. 4 tube. Of interest are the collapsible berths shown triced up against the reload racks. (Gus Britton)

▶ The wardroom in HMS *Tribune*, showing the leather seats which doubled as bunks. The 'Night Rounds Book' propped up on the bulkhead is serving as the wardroom's rough wine book with the injunction 'Stick 'Em Down' written on the cover. (IWM A.10913)

▶ The maze of pipes covering the deckhead of *Tribune*'s control room. The view is looking aft with the blowing panel on the left-hand side of the photograph. The voicepipe at lower right leads up to the bridge. (IWM A.10895)

▶ *Tribune*'s control room looking forward, with the hydroplane operators' positions on the port side and the steering position on the forward bulkhead. (IWM A.10903)

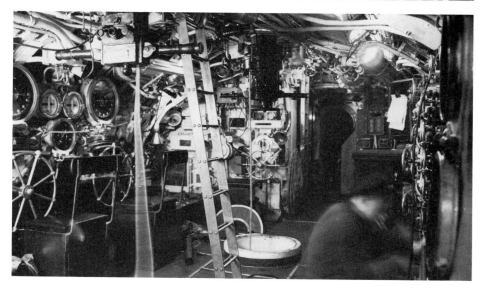

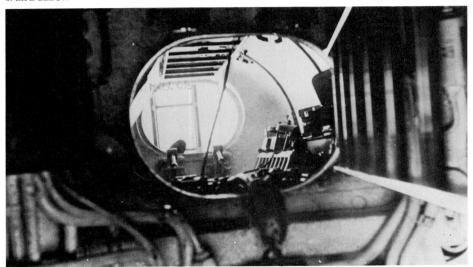

◀
View looking directly up the conning tower from *Tribune*'s control room. During a quick dive by *Talisman* in April 1942 seven men and a Bren gun were crammed into a similar space in their haste to get below. No fewer than four of the men had a part of their bodies sticking through the lower hatch into the control room: one can but hope that the safety catch on the Bren gun was 'on'! (IWM A.10926)

◀
Trident's bridge in 1940. Note the engine room telegraphs set on the forward edge of the attack periscope standard, the seaman coming up through the upper hatch, chart table on the port side and upper steering position with gyro compass repeater.

◀
A similar view of *Trump*'s bridge as she sails for the UK in November 1945. The submarine is no longer fitted with a steering position or chart table on the bridge. Note also the 'Jolly Roger' flying from the raised search periscope, the open gun tower hatch and the four bridge torpedo sights used when firing on the surface.

This was an eminently practicable arrangement since the stokers were near the engines and did not have to move the length of the submarine to reach their posts with all the attendant problems of upsetting the trim. Life in this after messdeck had its disadvantages: 'It was very noisy when the engines were running and there was a constant smell of diesel.'[12]

The Cammell Laird-built boats had a larger after end than the others. J. K. Chapman, a stoker in *Trident* (Lieutenant-Commander G. M. Sladen) remembered that: 'There was a long "after end" in *Trident* and all stokers had their own bunk. I've no recollection of "hot-bunking" on *Trident*. There was a small table each side of the messdeck and with a third of the stokers always on watch it didn't work out too bad although it became cramped in harbour when all the stokers piled in for a meal or a cuppa!'[13] However, T. J. Soar, inhabiting similar accommodation in *Tally-Ho* (Vickers) in the immediate post-war period remembers that: 'One graduated from the bale of rags between the HP Compressor and the LP Blower, to below the mess deck table, then on to the table, then to the worst bunk and eventually, when I became killick [senior leading hand] of the mess, to the best bunk.'[14]

T boats served in every theatre of operations and in every climate from the North Cape to the Malacca Straits. Each brought variable degrees of unpleasantness for the crew. In northern waters condensation was the principal problem. Stoker Chapman recalled that while *Trident* (Lieutenant-Commander G. M. Sladen) was working from Murmansk there was a '1½inch wave of water permanently rolling across the messdeck'.[15] In the Mediterranean the problem was the high level of humidity. Commander A. C. C. Miers of *Torbay* complained in August 1941 that, 'The submarine was very sticky and unpleasant when submerged. Any movement brought on sweating and a feeling of lassitude.'[16] This complaint was echoed by *Triumph*'s CO, Commander W. Woods, who noted that it was particularly unpleasant at periscope depth, but cooler if the boat was taken to below 80 feet.[17] The fitting of de-humidifiers helped to reduce sweating and condensation and were particularly useful in home waters where *Tuna* (Lieutenant-Commander M. K. Cavanagh-Mainwaring) was the first to report on their effectiveness.[18]

To be really effective the de-humidifiers had to be run for about ten hours a day so that the air would be fairly dry. However, the motor for the de-humidifier was sited in the seamen's mess forward and gave out such a lot of heat when running that although conditions throughout the rest of the boat were bearable, in the messdeck it was decidedly uncomfortable! Moreover the de-humidifiers were also extremely noisy: one CO compared their racket as akin to the 'wrath of God'.[19]

These arrangements were completely inadequate for the tropics where for sheet unpleasantness nothing beat the Malacca Straits where the ambient seawater temperature was about 80°F. The first T boat to venture into these waters was *Trusty* (Lieutenant-Commander W. D. A. King) in December 1941 and endured a dreadful time with the average temperature in the boat about 96°F – without any form of air conditioning other than the noisy de-humidifiers.[20] Those T boats sent out to Ceylon in 1943 experienced similar problems. *Templar*'s CO, Lieutenant D. J. Beckley, wrote in October 1943 that, '. . . prickly heat was rampant and there were several cases of boils and blood poisoning . . . lassitude was general after the first week and there is no doubt whatever that a *cooling system is absolutely essential if the standard of efficiency is to be maintained*'.[21] In *Trespasser* (Lieutenant-Commander R. M. Favell) the average temperature in the control room when dived was 94°F and Favell noted that nearly 10 per cent of his ship's company would have to stand off the next patrol.[22]

The solution was the fitting of Freon air-conditioning units which drew the air through a cooling and drying plant before discharging it through the boat's normal ventilation trunking. To reduce sweating in the boat all pipes and ventilation ducts were thoroughly lagged. A further refinement in T boats not found in other submarines was the fitting of separate punkah louvres to individual bunks by means of small branches from the main supply trunking. Air-conditioning arrangements in T boats were standardized by 1944 as two de-humidifiers for the Group One boats, one de-humidifier forward and one Freon unit aft for the Group Two and all Group Three boats except *Totem*, *Truncheon*, *Turpin*, *Token*, *Thermopylae*, *Teredo* and *Tabard* which were fitted with two Freon units, one forward and one aft.[23]

During an attack or when being hunted by enemy forces, all non-essential equipment had to be turned off both to avoid making noise and to conserve the battery, conditions under those circumstances rapidly became very unpleasant. Charles Deleay, an LTO an *Tantalus* (Lieutenant-Commander H. S. Mackenzie), recalled: 'I was on duty in the motor room during one attack and the temperature exceeded 130°F. I had to sit at the forward end of the engine room and make a quick dash back to the motor switches if a change of speed was ordered.'[24] The boats working from Fremantle enjoyed somewhat better conditions: the climate was drier and they spent more time on the surface due to the long passages to and from patrol areas.

The medical side of matters was catered for by the commanding officer and the coxswain who both had rudimentary medical training. An emergency medical kit containing simple antibiotics (M&B powder), antiseptics, morphia and some simple instruments was carried together with a small booklet of instructions. The book was an eminently practical publication with simple step-by-step instructions. For some reason, however, the book was withdrawn during the war leaving commanding officers with no guidance at all. The medical log of HMS *Terrapin*[25] shows the day-to-day medical chores of the coxswain. Boils, skin rashes and minor cuts which rapidly became infected in the none-too-clean atmosphere of a submarine, provided most of his work although one individual's ailment was described in terms which would hardly figure in the *Lancet* as 'shits and f-d up in general'.[26]

The brutal truth was that very little could be done for a seriously wounded man. Thus when Lieutenant Dennis Adams, *Tally-Ho*'s (Commander L. W. A. Bennington) gunnery officer, was severely wounded by a cannon shell which richocheted off the periscope standards during a night action with a Japanese submarine-chaser, there was little that Bennington or his coxswain, CPO 'Ginger' Ridley, could do other than administer morphia and make him comfortable. Adams died and was buried at sea in a simple but moving ceremony in which Bennington read the service to his ship's company assembled in the control room.

On one occasion in a T boat, help was at hand. On 23 March 1945 while on patrol in the West Java Sea, *Telemachus*'s (Commander W. D. A. King) engineer officer, Lieutenant-Commander (E) H. T. Meadows, was severely injured while working on a defective bearing on the port engine, his right hand being nearly severed at the wrist. Commander King sent details of the accident to Fremantle and was ordered to make for a rendezvous where an RAAF Catalina carrying a doctor would collect the injured officer. The rendezvous was made, *Telemachus* making most of the four-day passage on the surface to ensure a good supply of fresh air while Lieutenant-Commander Meadows had to 'submit to our amateur efforts'.[27] The Catalina was able to land alongside *Telemachus* and Lieutenant-Commander Meadows was speedily transferred while a USAAF Liberator provided cover overhead. Meadows' hand had to be amputated, but had he remained in *Telemachus* the consequences might well have been fatal.

Once the medical handbook had been withdrawn, the little medical knowledge imparted to a submarine commander could be a positive menace. *Thule*'s commander, Lieutenant-Commander A. C. Mars, was faced with a difficult situation when a number of his crew began to go down with the same symptoms: subnormal temperature, shaking of the limbs, stomach cramps and acute diarrhoea. Armed with little more than a first aid pamphlet, Mars and his engineer officer, Lieutenant C. L. Bedale, reached the same conclusion – that they had a possible cholera epidemic on their hands. Their worst fears were realized when Stoker Acton died. Mars was in a terrible dilemma and reluctantly signalled his suspicions to Ceylon. The reaction was swift: *Thule* was ordered to leave patrol and rendezvous with the destroyer *Terpsichore* which would be carrying medical staff and a complete spare crew. On boarding the submarine, the medical staff established that the ailment was severe heat exhaustion rather than cholera.[28] A little knowledge was a dangerous thing.

Little changed in the post-war period as regards habitability for the men serving in T boats: indeed it was one aspect of these remarkable submarines that remained unaltered. For the T-Conversions, however, a considerably enlarged complement was carried – 68 in all:

Executive Department:	Number borne
Lieutenant-Commander in command	1
Lieutenants RN	2
Lieutenant or Sub-Lieutenant, RN	1
Petty Officers	3
Leading Seamen	5
Able Seamen	13
Signalman	1
PO Telegraphist	1
Leading Telegraphist	1
Telegraphists	2
Engineering Department:	
Lieutenant-Commander (E) or Lieutenant (E)	1
Chief ERA	1
ERA	3
Mechanician	1
CPO Stoker	1
PO Stoker	1
Leading Stokers	5
Stokers	14
Electrical Department:	
Lieutenant (L)	1
Electrical Artificer	1
Electrician	1
Leading Electrician	2
Electrician's Mate	3
Radio Electrician	1
Others:	
Sick Berth Attendant	1
Leading Cook	1
Leading Steward	1[29]

The changes, notably a much larger engineering department and the introduction of an electrical department, reflected the greater emphasis placed on electrical equipment: radars, improved sonar and of course the much bigger battery. The carrying of an SBA, the professional equivalent of a State Registered Nurse, reflected the greater amount of time these boats would be spending dived and out of contact with professional advice ashore. The amateur ministrations of commanding officer and coxswain, however well intentioned, could not be tolerated in the peacetime navy.

To accommodate all these extras the torpedo stowage compartment now became a fully fledged messdeck, while not losing its other functions, and was fitted with proper bunks. A 1962 photograph of *Tiptoe*'s torpedo stowage compartment shows an additional twelve bunks fitted in two parallel rows, six a side and looking decidedly cramped.

Greater habitability was essential in a Conversion or Streamline since the boat would be spending far longer periods dived. A compartment created under the after end of the control room contained two Freon plants together with the associated ventilation fans. A 9-inch

▲
The galley onboard
Tribune: food for all the
ship's company was
cooked here. (IWM A.10914)

▶
Leading Chef Beeden (left)
and Telegraphist Appleton
display their handiwork
onboard *Tribune* in 1941.
Appleton later survived
the sinking of *Tempest* in
February 1942. (Royal Navy
Submarine Museum)

TO OPERATE W.C. DISCHARGE.

1. CHARGE AIR BOTTLE AND OPEN SEA AND N.R. VALVES
2. OPEN FLUSH INLET VALVE WITH CARE.
3. FREE LEVER AND BRING TO PAUSE.
4. BRING LEVER TO FLUSHING.
5. BRING LEVER TO DISCHARGE.
6. BRING LEVER TO PAUSE.
7. RETURN LEVER TO NORMAL AND LOCK.
8. CLOSE ALL VALVES.

▲
Brass plate giving instructions for blowing the heads in HMS *Thermopylae*. The plate was clearly produced by the Dockyard (*Thermopylae* was built at Chatham) since the forbidden word 'close' is used – 'shut' being the preferred term. (Royal Navy Submarine Museum)

▼
An RAAF Catalina alongside HMS *Telemachus* on 27 March 1945 for the transfer of the submarine's badly injured engineer officer, Lieutenant-Commander (E) H. T. Meadowes. (Royal Navy Submarine Museum)

▶
Tiptoe's fore ends in October 1962, showing how the collapsible berths were replaced by proper bunks inboard of the reload rails.

diameter trunk also led to this space from the snort induction mast in order to permit a proportion of the incoming air to be used for general ventilation. A gash ejector was fitted since it was no longer possible to simply ditch it over the conning tower every night and the Admiralty ruled that use of the torpedo tubes for this purpose was unacceptable.[30]

Accommodation spaces were brightened up by the use of Formica and other modern materials, but it could not be claimed that life in a T Conversion was comfortable. *Totem*'s CO remembered being 'deeply depressed'[31] when American officers went to sea with the boat since the standards of accommodation in US submarines were infinitely higher and their boats were not built of such downgraded wartime materials. Conditions in *Totem* were '. . . pretty squalid, there was no doubt about it. I would hardly pretend it was comfortable for anybody'.[32]

Attitudes to life in a T boat are somewhat paradoxical. The conditions were cramped, squalid and would often make a landsman blanch. However, the fact that whole ship's company, from commanding officer to ordinary seaman, were living in the same conditions, bred a sense of camaraderie not found in any other branch of the Service which more than compensated for the discomfort.

6. War 1939–45: Worth their Weight in Gold

Less than two years after HMS *Triton* was launched, Britain was at war. T boats were engaged in every type of submarine operation in every theatre of war. Each theatre had its own distinct characteristics yet there was a certain common ground between them. British submarines fought a very different war from that conducted by the U-boats in the Atlantic, or American submarines in the Pacific. There were no ill-protected convoys for British submarines to ravage, and no opportunities to wage a strategic campaign against Axis merchant shipping. Instead British submariners were faced with long and often unrewarding patrols in waters close to enemy bases and which were extensively mined. When targets did appear they moved under heavy escort and air cover.

On 10 September 1939, *Triton* (Lieutenant-Commander H. P. De C. Steele) was on patrol off Norway when she sighted another submarine on the surface. Steele challenged the other vessel three times using the Aldis lamp and then fired a signal grenade which burst correctly. When the other submarine failed to respond to the four challenges, Steele fired both bow externals and scored one hit. Whatever elation *Triton*'s crew may have felt at achieving their first success disappeared immediately when two survivors were picked up who proved to be the commanding officer of HMS *Oxley*, Lieutenant-Commander H. G. Bowerman, and a signalman. *Oxley* had been occupying the adjoining patrol billet but was considerably out of position. *Oxley* had seen *Triton*'s rifle grenade burst and her OOW claimed to have made the reply to *Triton*'s challenge. *Oxley* also fired a rifle grenade which tragically failed to work. A subsequent inquiry completely exonerated Lieutenant-Commander Steele, who had acted quite correctly, but the incident cast a pall over *Triton*, hitherto a very happy boat.[1]

Triumph (Lieutenant-Commander J. W. McCoy) was on patrol NE of Helgoland on 26 December 1939 when the OOW sighted a drifting mine ahead. The helm was put over, but the mine struck her on the port side of the stem. To those on the conning tower the 'explosion was very heavy with a sheet of flame 50-feet high', but to those inside the boat the explosion was felt as a 'loud metallic-sounding crash as though a giant had battered our keel with a jumbo-sized sledge-hammer'.[2] One seaman, A. B. Woods, remained asleep in his hammock in the torpedo stowage compartment throughout. The crew went to emergency stations and a survey showed that apart from damage to the steering gear all was well

aft of the watertight bulkhead leading to the tube space. The door leading through into the tube space was cautiously opened and the forward watertight bulkhead was found to be split and leaking. The leaks were plugged with wood and the flow of water staunched sufficiently that it could be kept under control by continuous pumping. *Triumph* was in a serious position, in enemy waters and unable to dive, but air cover in the form of Coastal Command Hudsons arrived and two days later *Triumph* limped into Rosyth where the extent of her injuries could be ascertained.

The bows had been completely blown away from the stem to No. 8 frame – a distance of 18 feet – along with two-thirds of the two bow external torpedo tubes. The six internal tubes were forced back about six inches and the bow caps were either shattered or completely missing. Most remarkable was the fact that all eight tubes had been loaded with torpedoes ready for firing and it says much for the design of the pistols that none of them exploded.

The beginning of the Norwegian Campaign in April 1940 saw *Thistle, Triton, Truant, Triad, Trident, Tetrarch, Taku* and *Tarpon* fully employed. *Triton*, now in the hands of Lieutenant-Commander E. F. Pizey, had the mortifying experience of missing *Lützow* and *Blücher* with a full, ten-torpedo salvo on 8 April 1940. During the next two days, Pizey is reported to have hardly spoken a word without swearing. But on 10 April he fired his remaining six torpedoes at a convoy and sank three ships: *Friedeman* of 5,219GRT; *Wiebert* of 3,648GRT and *Rau 6* of 324GRT.[3]

Truant (Lieutenant-Commander C. H. Hutchinson) torpedoed the German cruiser *Karlsruhe* (6,650 tons, nine 6-inch guns) on 9 April 1940 in the North Sea while homeward bound from Oslo. Hutchinson fired all ten tubes from abaft the beam and heard three explosions although German records note only one hit: *Karlsruhe* was later finished off by the torpedo-boat *Grief*. The result of this attack was that *Truant* had to endure a serious counter-attack by the escorts which caused many leaks and damage to machinery. Eventually, after a 19-hour dive, with the battery nearly exhausted and breathing in the submarine extremely difficult, she was able to surface. Hutchinson was then repeatedly forced to dive because of aircraft and was not able to report the attack until 1800 on 11 April: 'Defects rapidly being made good. Six torpedoes left. Morale High. Shall I return to patrol?' To which he received the reply from Vice-Admiral (S), Vice-Admiral Sir Max Horton, 'All in good time. I want to see you first.'[4]

Tetrarch (Lieutenant-Commander R. G. Mills), on her first patrol, was at the receiving end of an attack which kept the submarine down for 43 hours. *Tetrarch* had dived at 0250 on 23 April and at 1842 attacked a large merchant ship escorted by three destroyers off Hallo. The torpedoes missed, but the three destroyers came steaming down the torpedo tracks in line abreast and the first pattern of depth-charges was dropped at 1843. Mills took *Tetrarch* to between 300/350 feet and during the next three hours thirty charges were dropped. At 2000 Mills attempted to creep away, but this brought another barrage of depth-charges. By 2220 all seemed quiet, so Mills decided to surface and 'if no A/S craft were close . . . run for it (or) if one trawler (trawlers were heard to take over the hunt at about 2030] only were close to engage in gun action'. By this time there was a pressure of 5–6 inches in the boat due to the internal venting of A, Q and Z tanks, and so when surfacing the conning tower hatch was securely lashed: '. . . even so the CO floated in the conning tower for an apparently interminable period'. The foul air meant there was a delay in starting the engines, but soon *Tetrarch* was heading off with the diesels doing 400 revs, every fan and blower working flat out and the gun's crew closed up ready for action. Two minutes later Mills had to dive on sighting two trawlers dead ahead. Mills later described the period between 2223 and 2310 as 'tense' with charges exploding with great frequency, one of which caused the engine room hatch to lift and water to cascade into the engine room.

At 2310 *Tetrarch* porpoised between 400 feet and the surface due to Z tank being improperly vented on diving. Mills had ordered A, Q and Z to be flooded, but Z was blown completely. *Tetrarch* assumed a 20° bow

◄ A remarkable photograph showing *Triumph's* bows after hitting a mine on 26 December 1939. Two live torpedoes can just be seen in Nos. 2 and 4 tubes. (Royal Navy Submarine Museum)

► The German cruiser *Karlsruhe* sunk by HMS *Truant* in the North Sea on 9 April 1940.

▲ HMS *Trident* returns to her depot ship in Holy Loch in March 1942 following her deployment to the Arctic in support of the Russians. (IWM A.7934)

◄ The German cruiser *Prinz Eugen*, torpedoed by *Trident* on 23 February 1942. The photograph shows her hastily repaired stern before her return to Germany for more permanent repairs. (IWM/ Korvettenkapitän Paul Schmalenbach)

down angle which could not be checked by blowing 1 and 2 main ballast tanks. She shot to the surface and remained up for about half a minute before diving to 350 feet where Mills managed to catch a stopped trim using Q tank. There was nothing for it but to sit the attack out, so all machinery was stopped, except the forward hydroplanes motor. The depth-charging continued until midnight when Mills ordered the forward hydroplane motor to be stopped. It appeared that it was this noise which was keeping the enemy in contact, for their HE now grew fainter. *Tetrarch* did not surface until 2130 on 24 April by which time many of her crew were in an exhausted condition, one man having to breathe oxygen via a DSEA set for the last twelve hours of the dive. A witness of *Tetrarch*'s return to harbour noted that her crew looked physically and mentally exhausted, evidently still suffering from the effects of their ordeal.[5]

The Norwegian Campaign also saw the first war losses. *Tarpon* and *Thistle* were lost on the same day, 10 April 1940. *Thistle* (Lieutenant-Commander W. Haselfoot) was torpedoed by U4 (Kapitänleutnant Hans-Peter Hinsch). Nine hours later *Tarpon* (Lieutenant-Commander H. J. Caldwell) was depth-charged to destruction by the German Q-ship, *Schiff 40*.[6]

Patrols in the Bay of Biscay were established in July 1940 following the German occupation of the French Atlantic coast ports. *Tigris* was the first to patrol this beat followed by *Talisman*, *Thunderbolt*, *Truant*, *Taku*, *Torbay*, *Tribune*, *Trident* and *Tuna*. These patrols, known as the 'Iron Ring', became doubly important with the arrival of German capital ships, but were discontinued after *Scharnhorst*, *Gneisenau* and *Prinz Eugen* departed for Germany in February 1942 in the famous 'Channel Dash'. The patrols were not without their successes. *Thunderbolt* (Lieutenant-Commander C. B. Crouch) sank the Italian submarine *Tarantini* on 15 December 1940, the first of fourteen Axis submarines to be sunk by a T boat. *Trident* (Lieutenant-Commander G. M. Sladen) enjoyed a spirited gun action with U31 on 8 October 1940 and claimed to have damaged the latter's conning tower. *Tigris* (Lieutenant-Commander H. F. Bone) missed two large Italian submarines, *Reginaldo Giuliani* and *Maggiore Baracca*, bound for Bordeaux on 5 October 1940, but disposed of the *Michele Bianchi* off the Gironde on 5 July 1941. T-boat operations in the Bay of Biscay did not come to a halt with the suspension of formal patrols in the area: all boats on passage to the Mediterranean or the Far East passed through the Bay and they had to be on their guard; *Tally-Ho*, on passage to Gibraltar between 18 July and 7 August 1943 had three U-boat sightings to brighten her passage, but no attack was possible.

On completion of their operations in the Bay of Biscay, *Tigris* (Lieutenant-Commander H. F. Bone) and *Trident* (Lieutenant-Commander G. M. Sladen) ventured up into the Arctic, arriving at Polyarnoe on 4 and 10 August 1941 respectively. Their task would be to interdict the steady stream of German troop convoys passing along the north Norwegian coast. Soviet submariners showed great interest in the British boats though it is doubtful whether the rigid political system which discouraged personal initiative under which they operated allowed them to benefit from the experience. During *Trident*'s last patrol, she damaged the German cruiser *Prinz Eugen* on 23 February 1942. *Prinz Eugen* was proceeding to Bergen with *Admiral Scheer* and they were sighted aft of *Trident*'s port beam. Sladen executed a retiring turn and intended to fire seven torpedoes while remaining on the surface, but after three had been fired decided to dive. On diving he found that his orders had been misinterpreted and that check fire had been ordered after the third torpedo had been fired. No matter, one of three torpedoes found its mark and blew the cruiser's stern off. Good damage control ensured her safe arrival at Trondheim, but she had to return to Germany for proper repairs and would not be operational until January 1943.

Convoy escort duty must rank as one of the most wasteful tasks in which the T Class were employed. *Taku*, *Tribune*, *Thunderbolt* and *Talisman* all formed the North Atlantic Escort Force, part of the 2nd Submarine Flotilla, and helped reinforce the escort for the HX/SC convoys running between Halifax and the UK. *Thunderbolt* (Lieutenant-Commander C. B. Crouch) had a particularly thin time of it, being fired on by the armed merchant cruiser HMS *Canton*, neither being aware of the other's presence in the area, on 24 February 1941, and then missing U557 with a six-tube salvo on 15 June 1941. The failure of *Thunderbolt*'s attack on U557 was disappointing because it was one of the first interceptions resulting from ULTRA intelligence, but her torpedo drill was not up to a high standard of training as a result of having wasted so much time on convoy escort duty. The 2nd Flotilla was disbanded in July 1941: *Thunderbolt* and *Talisman* proceeding to the Mediterranean; *Taku* and *Tribune* returning to the UK.

But in the main, T-boat operations in Home Waters consisted of patrols off the Norwegian Coast. After the decision in September 1943 that all new and refitted T boats should be sent direct to the Far East, their involvement in Home Waters became minimal. New construction T boats would undertake one, sometimes two, working-up patrols in Home Waters before proceeding to the Far East. The hoped-for prize in such patrols being the German battleship *Tirpitz*. Such operations were largely defensive in nature: in the 'anti-*Tirpitz*' patrols, commanders were forbidden to fire at anything other than the 'Lone Queen of the North' herself. The other aim of these patrols was to catch U-boats heading out into the Atlantic or returning to bases in Norway. Three U-boats were sunk by a T boat: U644 sunk by *Tuna* (Lieutenant D. S. R. Martin) on 7 April 1943; U308 sunk by *Truculent* (Lieutenant-Commander R. L. Alexander) on 4 June 1943 and U486 sunk by *Tapir* (Lieutenant J. C. Y. Roxburgh) on 12 April 1945. Merchant ship targets were seldom encountered on these patrols, but occasionally a submarine could achieve a number of successes. *Taku* (Lieutenant A. J. Pitt) sank three ships: *Rheinhausen* of 6,298GRT, *H.Fritzen* of 4,818GRT and *Bornhofen* of 3,000GRT in a patrol in February 1943 when Pitt deliberately took the boat into Bommelfiord.[7]

From September 1940 T boats began to operate in the Mediterranean. *Truant, Triad, Tetrarch* and *Triton*, later reinforced by *Triumph*, were the first to arrive. T boats operated with the 1st Flotilla from Alexandria, Haifa and Beirut, with the 8th Flotilla from Gibraltar, and later Algiers, and also from Malta where they came under the operational control of the famous 10th Flotilla without being formally part of it. In all 24 T boats: *P.311, Tactician, Taku, Talisman, Taurus, Tempest, Templar, Tetrarch, Thorn, Thrasher, Thunderbolt, Tigris, Torbay, Traveller, Trespasser, Triad, Tribune, Trident, Triton, Triumph, Trooper, Truant, Trusty,* and *Turbulent* served in this theatre.

The T class were ideally suited for the Mediterranean: '. . . they had the endurance and range to be really effective because there were very long distances from one's bases to get into enemy-controlled waters'.[8] Initially their operations were directed at traffic running between Italy and North Africa. The German invasion of Yugoslavia and Greece in April 1941 meant that operations were extended into the Aegean right up

to the entrance to the Dardanelles, where *Torbay* (Lieutenant-Commander A. C. C. Miers) sank the Vichy French tanker *Alberta* on 6 June 1941 off Cape Helles. The Adriatic was another area of operations in which *Tetrarch, Thorn, Thrasher, Thunderbolt, Tigris, Traveller, Triumph, Trooper* and *Turbulent* were involved.

The new arrivals lost no time in getting into their stride. *Truant,* now under command of Lieutenant-Commander H. A. V. Haggard, sank the 8,459GRT *Provvidenza* on her first patrol. From September 1940 until December 1941, when she went to the Far East, *Truant* carried out eleven patrols in the Mediterranean during which she sank one small destroyer and eight merchant ships totalling 27,553GRT, together with a 1,080-ton naval auxiliary which was adjudged to have 'died of fright' having run herself ashore despite being missed by *Truant*'s torpedoes. When in May 1941 *Truant* departed for a well-earned refit in the USA, Admiral Sir Andrew Cunningham noted that: '. . . the operations of HMS/M *Truant* have been a model of daring and enterprise, tempered with just the right degree of caution'.[9] One example will suffice. On 19 March 1941 *Truant* entered the small harbour of Burat-el-Sun on the North African coast to sink a tanker lying there. Torpedoes were fired at a range of 400 yards, but ran under since the tanker had discharged her cargo and

▲
Three T-class submarines
alongside the depot ship
Titania in bleak Scottish
surroundings in late 1941.
The inboard boat is
Turbulent on work-up
before sailing for the
Mediterranean; the centre
boat is *Tuna* and the
outboard boat is *Tigris*.
(IWM A.6585)

◄
HMS *Truant*'s 'Jolly Roger':
each white bar represents
a target sunk by torpedo,
the stars around the
crossed guns are for
successful gun actions
and the dagger represents
a special operation. (IWM
A.13143)

▶
Tuna's 'Jolly Roger' in
August 1943 testifies to her
success in the anti U-boat
patrols: she has claimed
four U-boats as sunk and
wears four 'U's on her
'Jolly Roger'. In fact only
one of the attacks was
confirmed: the sinking of
U644 on 7 April 1943. (IWM
A.18932)

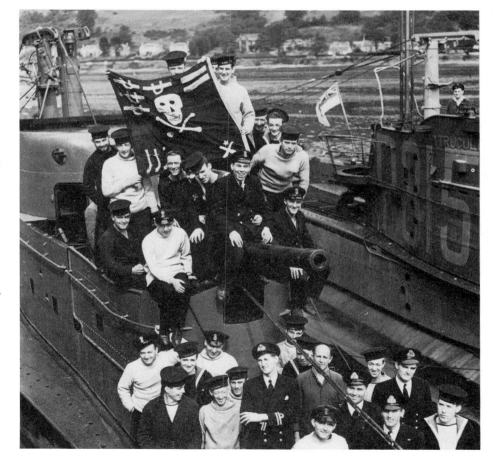

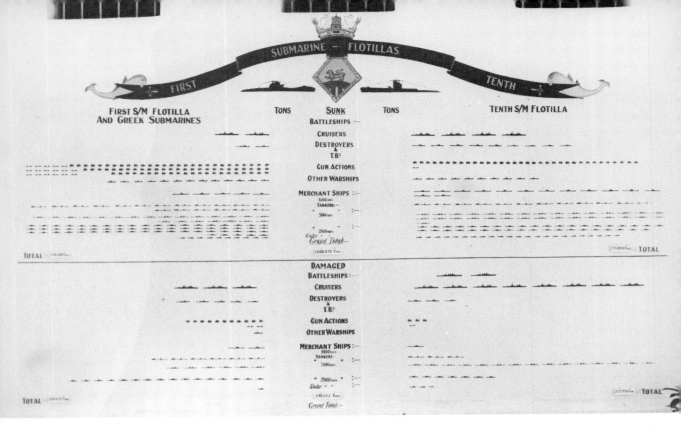

was riding higher in the water than Haggard thought. *Truant* was now faced with the problem of how to extricate herself from the confined harbour: 'It was necessary to turn on the propellers, at the same time coming to full buoyancy, in order to clear the enemy's quarter. As the conning tower came abreast the after deckhouse and a few yards from it, a man came out, leant over the guardrail and had a good deal to say. With a cry of "Il Duce!" *Truant* passed out of earshot and proceeded out of the harbour.'[10]

Rommel's armies depended on petrol being brought by sea and therefore the sinking of a tanker, such as the 2,474GRT *Persiano* sunk by *Tetrarch* (Lieutenant-Commander R. G. Mills) on 12 April 1941, could have results for the Desert Campaign far out of proportion to the loss of the ship herself. *Thrasher* (Lieutenant H. S. Mackenzie) sank two petrol carriers at a crucial stage in the war: the 3,337-ton naval yacht *Diana* on 29 June 1942, hit by 4 out of a 6-torpedo salvo; and the 1,580-ton *Padenna* on 4 September 1942. The explosion of both ships left little doubt that petrol was their cargo. The Axis obligingly aided British submariners by adhering to the same convoy routes for periods of up to three months at a time, allowing submarines to be deployed across likely routes. However the Ts' low speed meant that attacks on convoys were generally a matter of opportunity rather than policy. *Turbulent*'s (Commander J. W. Linton) attack on a convoy on the night of 28/29 May 1942 may be regarded as a model. Linton stalked the convoy and manoeuvred for a dawn attack and at 0600 four torpedoes were fired. Two struck the

Italian destroyer *Pessagno*, the third struck the 3,170GRT *Capo Arma* – both ships later sinking – while the fourth torpedo ran wild, circling over the submarine.[11]

It was for the relentless pursuit of an Axis troop convoy that Lieutenant-Commander A. C. C. Miers, commanding officer of HMS *Torbay*, was awarded the Victoria Cross: one of four VCs to be awarded to officers and men of T boats serving in the Mediterranean. On 4 March 1942 Miers sighted a northbound convoy of four troopships entering Corfu Roads. He took *Torbay* into the harbour in search of the troopships, only to find that they had sailed. Nevertheless he spent twenty hours inside the heavily defended anchorage and had the insouciance to charge his batteries while lying on the surface before torpedoing two ships, sinking one and damaging the other. Miers' VC was gazetted on 7 July 1942.[12]

Against Italian naval units their major success was scored by *Triumph* (Commander W. J. Woods) when she damaged the Italian cruiser *Bolzano* on 26 August 1941. *Triumph* was tasked for a special operation to land commandos to blow up a viaduct near Palermo and had been ordered to a position off Messina to intercept enemy surface forces. At 0600 on the 28th a battleship, two cruisers and a large number of destroyers were sighted. Because of the extra men aboard with their stores and folboats, *Triumph* had sailed with only two torpedoes. Woods' task was not made any easier by various mechanical difficulties which were making themselves felt in *Triumph* including a burned out

◄
A mural at the submarine base at Beirut showing the record of success for the 1st and 10th Submarine Flotillas. The 1st Flotilla was composed largely of T-boats. (IWM A.18056)

▲
The Italian destroyer *Emanuele Pessagno* sunk by *Turbulent* during a classic attack on a convoy on the night of 28/29 May 1942. (Dr. Achille Rastelli)

▼
Commander A. C. C. Miers, the unconventional and ebullient commanding officer of HMS *Torbay*, awarded the Victoria Cross for his penetration of Corfu Roads in March 1942. (IWM A.10216)

ASDIC motor and a fogged search periscope. In poor visibility Woods fired both torpedoes at the last cruiser in the screen and was rewarded with a hit. *Bolzano* was slowed down but managed to make Messina. *Triumph* escaped an 'angry but indiscriminate'[13] counter-attack, but she was not able to surface to pass her enemy report until early evening, too late for action to be taken by other forces. This was the major success against Axis warships in the Mediterranean, although *Truant* sank the small destroyer *Alcione* on 11 December 1941 off Crete.

Five Italian submarines were sunk by T boats in the Mediterranean: *Salpa* sunk by *Triumph* (Lieutenant-Commander W. J. Woods) on 27 June 1941; *Jantina* sunk by *Torbay* (Commander A. C. C. Miers) on 5 July 1941; *Medusa* sunk by *Thorn* (Lieutenant-Commander R. G. Norfolk) on 30 January 1942; *Porfido* sunk by *Tigris* (Lieutenant-Commander G. Colvin) on 6 December 1942 and the large minelayer *Pietro Micca* sunk by *Trooper* (Lieutenant G. S. Clarabut) on 29 July 1943. All of these submarines were sunk while proceeding on the surface in broad daylight: an Axis habit which was described as 'truly reprehensible'.[14] The sinking of *Medusa* was a particularly serious blow for the Italian Navy. At the time of her loss *Medusa* was employed in taking embryo submarine commanding officers to sea for training. Lieutenant-Commander Norfolk had seen her leave Pola in the morning of 30 January and enter the protected waters off Brioni for exercises. *Thorn* remained in the area waiting for *Medusa* to return that evening which she duly did. Norfolk fired one torpedo

◄
The Italian cruiser *Bolzano* limps into Messina after being torpedoed by *Triumph* on 26 August 1941. (Dr. Achille Rastelli)

◄
Truant's torpedo strikes the Italian destroyer *Alcione* on 11 December 1941 off the coast of Crete. Note how close inshore the attack was conducted. (Royal Navy Submarine Museum)

►
HMS *Torbay* returns to Algiers in March 1943 during her second commission in the Mediterranean. *Torbay* was the highest-scoring T-class submarine with a total of 57,990 tons of Axis shipping. Inset shows her 'Jolly Rogers': two flags are shown; the foreground is that for *Torbay*'s first commission under Commander A. C. C. Miers, VC, and the other is for her second commission under Lieutenant R. J. Clutterbuck. (IWM A.15560/22574)

◄
The Italian submarine *Medusa*, sunk by HMS *Thorn* off Pola on 30 January 1942. (Dr. Achille Rastelli)

◄
The large Italian minelaying submarine *Pietro Micca* sunk by *Trooper* at the entrance to the Adriatic on 29 July 1943. *Micca* was returning to Brindisi with defects and the Italians unwisely switched on the coastal navigation lights to assist her passage, which gave Clarabutt the indication that a target was approaching. (Dr. Achille Rastelli)

which was sufficient to sink the small 600-ton vessel.

Many contacts were made with U-boats while both parties were submerged, but British submarines lacked the required fire control for attacks upon a submerged submarine. The nearest a T boat came to such an attack was on 14 August 1941 when *Talisman* (Lieutenant M. Willmott) proceeding dived from Malta to Alexandria heard the HE of another submerged submarine. Willmott fired three torpedoes at a range of 800 yards, but no hits were heard, fortunately because the 'target' was HMS *Otus*. *Talisman* remained in contact until *Otus* was heard to surface at dusk. A surface chase then followed with *Talisman* hoping to make a gun attack, but *Otus*'s lookouts sighted *Talisman* coming up from astern and fired off a recognition grenade. A subsequent inquiry found that *Talisman* was more than 10 miles off her routed track, but had not been warned of *Otus*'s likely presence.[15]

Thrasher (Lieutenant H. S. Mackenzie) had a very narrow escape from destruction during a patrol off Crete. On 16 February 1942 *Thrasher* had damaged a 3,000-ton supply ship which resulted in her being counter-attacked by ships and aircraft. Later that evening her CO recalled:

'We ran into a slight swell and began rolling slightly. I was in my bunk by then because everything seemed calm and I was woken up by a noise in the casing overhead every time we rolled. Not liking the sound of this, I told the OOW to send somebody down on to the casing to find out what it was and secure it. Five minutes later I got a report that there was what appeared to be a bomb lying on the casing and a hole in the side of the gun casing seemed to indicate that there was another inside the casing further aft.

'So I sent for the First Lieutenant (Lieutenant P. W. Roberts) and the Second Coxswain (PO T. W. Gould) and told them that they were to get rid of the bomb on the casing, drag it up to the bows and when we were ready I would go full astern and once we had stern way on they could lower it over the side and let go. They were then to look inside the casing and find out what the reason for the hole was. They reported another bomb wedged inside the casing on top of the pressure hull just abaft the gun. We got rid of the easy one first and

then they had to get inside the casing and crawl along for about 20 feet to get at the other bomb and once they got hold of it they had to drag it forward on their hands and knees the whole way. Eventually they ditched it over the bows.'[16]

This was a cold-blooded act of gallantry: if the bomb had exploded the submarine would have been destroyed. Both Lieutenant Roberts and PO Gould were subsequently recommended for and received the Victoria Cross, the award being gazetted on 9 June 1942.

Thrasher had sailed for that patrol on 13 February 1942, and her good fortune had dispelled any doubts about a possible jinx attached to sailing on the 13th of a month. Four months later, in July 1942, *Thrasher's* good luck was to be severely tested in an incident in which she was badly damaged: probably more severely than any T boat during the war. She left Port Said for patrol on the evening of 26 July 1942. Her commanding officer later recalled that they were:

'. . . proceeding on the surface zig-zagging with a safety corridor around us to prevent attack by friendly aircraft. At about 9pm I came down from the bridge to have supper thinking that everything was all settled: we were about 30 miles outside Port Said then, happily set on our way. I was sitting in my usual place at the wardroom table which was in the gangway as near to the control room as possible so that I could get out in a hurry if needed and I very clearly remember something telling me to get on the bridge and I got up and left the table without explaining why or in response to any request for me to go on the bridge. I was just going through the watertight bulkhead between the wardroom and the control room when there was the most God awful explosion and the next thing I remember was picking myself up from the after end of the control room up against the W/T office. During the course of getting up from there I remember seeing the ship's

galley range which was in the passageway abaft the wireless office leave the ship's side in a cloud of blue sparks.

'As I was picking myself up I heard the OOW, the First Lieutenant, give the order to dive and the drill was carried out, the vents were opened by the outside ERA although the lights had gone out and there were a lot of odd noises going on. I then heard the Bren gun on the bridge open fire so I knew they were all right up there. The signalman, lookouts and OOW came down and we dived. Reports were coming in of damage: quite clearly we had no electrical power, smoke was coming from the battery compartments, we had a fire in the battery [smoke and gas were coming from Nos. 2 and 3 batteries and No. 1 battery was on fire and later had to be flooded with distilled water] and we had to drop all the main fuses, but we sorted ourselves out. The gyro was humming like an angry bee and the magnetic compass was upside down and no good. It seemed to me that the best thing we could do would be to get back on the surface especially as the First Lieutenant thought it was a Swordfish which had attacked us.'

A Swordfish had attacked *Thrasher* and in the middle of a submarine sanctuary – an area where no attacks were permitted on submarines. The Swordfish, on A/S patrol and armed with four 250lb depth-charges, was either gravely out of position or in the heat of moment forgot that they were in a bombing restriction area. The Swordfish dropped all four charges: one fell on the port side abreast the fore hatch, the next two fell on the starboard side and the fourth was not seen to explode. The explosions lifted the stern so much that the bows went under water. *Thrasher's* CO continues:

'It was quite clear that we could not proceed with the patrol so we surfaced and then had to try and get our engines started with no electrical power which took a little time . . . We got the engines going but our main

problem was to keep afloat because the main ballast tanks were clearly leaking the whole time and we had to keep blowing them with high-pressure air since there was no electric power to use the LP blower and also we'd got no means of steering a proper course since all the compasses had gone. Fortunately it was a starlit night and I knew that Port Said was roughly south and I directed operations standing on the bridge with the Pole Star behind me saying "Port" and "Starboard" down the voicepipe. We then ran into one of the trawlers patrolling off Port Said and identified ourselves and staggered into Port Said on our last gasp of high-pressure air . . . our ballast tanks were awash.'[17]

Captain(S)1 later commented that 'the excellent construction was very severely tested and proved thoroughly sound[18] although some officials at the Admiralty expressed disappointment at the limited effects of the 250lb depth-charge! The list of damage to *Thrasher* covers two typewritten pages of foolscap in the DNC's analysis, most serious being the damage to the battery, only 30 of 336 cells remaining undamaged, and to the seam on the pressure hull between 87 and 88 frames where the planes were working slightly.

Further damage was caused by battery acid eating through into H tank, the magazine and the Coxswain's store.

Thrasher was a lucky submarine. The other side of this story of success is that thirteen T boats were sunk in the Mediterranean: more than half the number that operated there. These high losses reflect the tremendous odds the submarines were up against, rather than their unsuitability for this theatre. Vice-Admiral Sir Hugh Mackenzie, who commanded *Thrasher* in the Mediterranean, remembered that ' We had to go into heavily patrolled waters to do any good at all. We knew they were mined and as time went on the Axis powers became better and better in their anti-submarine methods and we were up against pretty good opposition'.[19]

The *modus operandi* of British submarines – diving by day even though this meant they could only cover about 120 miles and surfacing at night to charge – probably ensured the survival of many. Axis A/S forces accounted for five of the thirteen T boats sunk in the Mediterranean. *Triad* (Lieutenant-Commander G. S. Salt) was the first to go, sunk in a gun and torpedo

▶ HMS *Thrasher*'s 'Jolly Roger': eleven ships are shown as having been sunk by torpedo and seven with her gun. Two of the white bars represent ships carrying vital petrol for Axis armies in North Africa. (Royal Navy Submarine Museum)

◀ HMS *Thrasher* alongside the depot ship HMS *Medway*, showing the hole in her gun tower casing made by a German bomb which failed to explode. Petty Officer Gould stands in the hatch through which he and Lieutenant Roberts dragged the bomb before ditching it over the side. (IWM A.13571)

▶

HMS *Triad* on trials before the war. *Triad* was the first of thirteen T boats to be sunk in the Mediterranean, being sunk by the Italian S/M *Enrico Toti* in a gun and torpedo action on the night of 14/15 October 1940.

action on the night of 14/15 October 1940 against the Italian submarine *Enrico Toti* (Lieutenant-Commander Bandino Bandini) SW of Calabria. *Triad* was on patrol in the Gulf of Taranto and encountered *Toti* on the surface shortly after midnight. There was a brief but fierce gun engagement in which *Triad* scored two hits on *Toti*, which did little damage, and fired a torpedo which passed astern of the Italian boat. Both submarines closed each other, so close that *Toti*'s First Lieutenant could hear *Triad*'s bridge party speaking English. *Toti* now used her superiority in close-range weapons to force *Triad*'s bridge party and gun crew below: a tactic which apparently succeeded. But as *Triad* began to dive *Toti* scored two hits with her gun on *Triad*'s conning tower and also one hit with a torpedo, following which, *Triad* was observed to sink. *Triad* was the only British submarine to be sunk by an Italian submarine, and her loss is the only occasion in history when one submarine has sunk another in a surface action. *Toti*'s victim has generally been thought to have been HMS *Rainbow*, but recent research has established that it was *Triad* thus confirming Captain S. M. Raw's, Captain(S)1, original suspicion as to the cause of her loss.[20]

◀

Lieutenant-Commander Bandino Bandini (second from right wearing binoculars), commanding officer of *Enrico Toti*, with other members of his ship's company after sinking *Triad*. (Dr. Achille Rastelli)

▶

Tempest surfaces after having endured seven hours' of depth-charging by the Italian TB *Circe* on 13 February 1942. *Tempest* eventually sank as she was being taken in tow. (IWM HU.2278)

Tempest's loss resulted from an attack on an Italian tanker, *Lucania*, on 12 February by HMS *Una* (Lieutenant D. S. R. Martin). *Lucania* was taking fuel to Italian refugee ships in East Africa and had been given a 'safe conduct' by the British. The Italians instituted extra patrols to find the culprit, but found *Tempest* instead of *Una*. The torpedo-boat *Circe* (Lieutenant-Commander Stefanino Palmas) got an ECG (Ecogoniometro: the Italian equivalent of ASDIC) contact at 0315 on 13 February and proceeded to carry out a depth-charge attack which reduced the interior of *Tempest* to a shambles. At 0942 No. 3 battery began giving off large quantities of chlorine and Cavaye decided to surface. *Circe* saw *Tempest* come up at 0945 and opened fire with her machine-guns on two gallant men who tried to bring the submarine's 4-inch gun into action. *Tempest*'s crew abandoned the submarine and were picked up by *Circe*. The main vents had been opened and the scuttling charges set, but *Tempest* stubbornly remained afloat until 1605 when she sank stern first just as *Circe* had managed to place a boarding party aboard and secured a tow rope.

Thereafter *Tempest* (Lieutenant-Commander W. K. A. N. Cavaye) on 13 February 1942 by the Italian TB *Circe* in the Gulf of Taranto; *Thorn* (Lieutenant-Commander R. G. Norfolk) on 7 August 1942 by the Italian *De Pegaso* off Ghardvos Island, south of Crete; *Tigris* (Lieutenant G. R. Colvin) on 27 February 1943 by the German *UJ2210* SE of Capri; and *Thunderbolt* (Lieutenant-Commander C. B. Crouch) on 14 March 1943 by the Italian corvette *Cicogna* off Capo San Vito, Sicily were sunk. There were no survivors from *Thorn*, *Tigris* and *Thunderbolt*, but 24 officers and men survived from *Tempest*: Lieutenant-Commander Cavaye was not among them.

The Mediterranean was also extensively mined by the Axis, so much so that Captain G. C. Phillips, who commanded 10th Submarine Flotilla from January 1943, commented in September 1943, after studying Italian minelaying records, that '. . . it is difficult to know how our submarines could have operated had the positions of these fields been known previously'.[24] Mines are believed to have accounted for the remaining seven T boats sunk in the Mediterranean: *Triton* (Lieutenant G. C. I. Watkins) on or about 6 December 1940 in the southern Adriatic; *Tetrarch* (Lieutenant-Commander G. H. Greenway) presumed mined in the Sicilian Channel to the SW of Sicily on 27 October 1941 or off Caoli Island on 29 October 1941 en route for the UK and a well-

◄
HMS *Turbulent* at Algiers on 12 February 1943 after completion of a very successful patrol off Sicily. Just over a month later, she was lost off Corsica on her last patrol. The inboard boat is *Taku*. (IWM A.14795)

▼
HMS *Turbulent*'s 'Jolly Roger'. The flag carries additional symbols marking *Turbulent*'s train-wrecking activities and a truck for her bombardment of a German lorry park in North Africa. (IWM A.14794)

earned refit in the USA; *Triumph* (Lieutenant J. S. Huddart) on or about 31 December 1941 off Hydra; *Talisman* (Lieutenant-Commander M. Willmott) on or about 17 September 1942 in the Sicilian Channel; *Traveller* (Lieutenant-Commander D. St. Clair Ford) on or about 4 December 1942 while engaged in a reconnaissance of Taranto harbour; *P.311* (Commander R. D. Cayley) on or about 2 January 1943 off Maddalena, northern Sardinia during Operation 'Principal'; and *Trooper* (Lieutenant J. S. Wraith) on or about 10 October 1943 east of Leros. Evidence for these sinkings comes from known patrol routes and the positions of Axis minefields.

The loss of *Turbulent* is something of an enigma and deprived the Royal Navy of one of the most able submarine commanders of the Second World War. A former First Lieutenant remembered Commander J. W. 'Tubby' Linton as: '. . . very tough, stern chap outwardly with high standards and a strong disciplinarian. Inwardly I think he was a very kind, gentle man, but physically and mentally tough. He was very quick on his feet: when we were doing an attack he did most of it in his head regardless of what his instruments were saying. He had a good sense of humour but I think we were all a little frightened of him. I utterly trusted him because there was not much he didn't know about the submarine world or how to run a submarine in wartime.'[22]

Turbulent was on her eleventh, and last patrol in the Mediterranean before returning to the UK, when she was sunk. Linton had a roving brief in the Tyrrhenian Sea and after sinking the 865GRT *Vincenzo* off Calabria on 1 March headed north-west towards Giglio Island. An attack on the 450GRT mail ship *Principessa Mafalda* on 11 March eight miles off Bastia was unsuccessful and led to A/S patrols in the area being stepped-up. The A/S trawlers *Lido*, *Santa Rita* and *Teti II* with the anti-submarine launch *MAS.558* were ordered to conduct an A/S sweep off Bastia on 12 March. At 0910 in a position 4–12 miles ESE of Punta Arco, *Teti II* suddenly sighted first the periscope and then the conning tower of a submarine briefly emerging from the water as if the boat had temporarily lost trim. *Teti II* ran over the spot and dropped a pattern of eight depth-charges. The submarine was undoubtedly *Turbulent* since no other boats, Axis or Allied, were in the area. Since there was no definite evidence to prove that *Teti*'s attack had been successful, *Turbulent* was originally adjudged to have fallen victim to a mine off Maddalena on or about 14 March. However, an examination of post-war Italian records shows that there were no further reliable reports of submarine activity in *Turbulent*'s area after *Teti*'s attack on 12 March. In the absence of further information it must be presumed that *Teti*'s attack was successful. On 20 March *Turbulent* was given her homeward route to Algiers and ordered to acknowledge the signal. No reply was received and when she failed to arrive at Algiers on 23 March, she was declared overdue.[23] Commander Linton was posthumously awarded the VC, the award being gazetted on 25 May 1943. The award was not made for a particular engagement but rather for the relentless pressure which Linton exerted on the enemy. In *Turbulent* Linton sank one destroyer and twelve merchant ships totalling 33,345GRT together with a number of caiques.

In September 1941 Admiral Cunningham had said that every submarine that could be sent to the Mediterranean was 'worth its weight in gold'.[24] The role of British submarines in preventing the efficient supply of Axis armies in North Africa was crucial and the T boats played an important part in this campaign. But after the Italian armistice in September 1943, their operations were directed toward a third theatre of war – the Far East.

► Commander J. W. Linton (right), commanding officer of HMS *Turbulent* and posthumously awarded the Victoria Cross, with Lieutenant A. J. Pitt, commanding officer of HMS *Taku*: photograph taken at Beirut in 1942. (Commander A. J. Pitt)

7. War 1939–45: Submarines or Gunboats?

The Far East was the theatre for which the T class had been designed. Japan was an island empire, dependent on seaborne trade for the supply of raw materials, particularly oil. In the absence of a British battlefleet in the region, submarines would be expected to deal with the considerable Japanese Navy, hence the very large torpedo armament given to the T class. Operating from bases at Singapore or Hong Kong, the T class would have the range and endurance to patrol the South and East China Seas together with the Sea of Japan itself. Yet by the time any T boats could be spared for the Far East the situation had changed radically. The splendid bases at Singapore and Hong Kong from which submarines could have struck at the heart of Japan had surrendered: the nearest base for the conduct of operations was Ceylon.

After requests from Admiral Sir Geoffrey Layton, CinC Eastern Fleet, *Trusty* and *Truant* were detached from the Mediterranean Fleet in December 1941 and January 1942 respectively. *Trusty* arrived at Singapore on 31 January carrying extra personnel required for the establishment of a submarine base, but was forced to leave for Surabaya before the British surrendered on 15 February. *Trusty* and *Truant* operated for a while from Sourabaya with American and Dutch submarines, but in March 1942 were forced back to Ceylon. The next T boat to go east was *Trident* in July 1943, but she had to return to the UK with engine defects after one patrol. Although operations in the Mediterranean continued after the Italian armistice in September 1943, submarines could be spared for the Far East in greater numbers. *Templar*, *Trespasser*, *Tally-Ho*, *Taurus* and *Tactician* all arrived in September/October 1943 to join the 4th and reconstituted 8th Flotillas.

Their area of operations would be down the west coast of Malaya and the Malacca Straits between

◀
HMS *Trusty*'s crew poses with their 'Jolly Roger' on their return to the UK. *Trusty* had been the first T boat to go to the Far East, but had a disappointing time. (IWM A.17540)

▲
The Japanese cruiser *Kuma* sunk by *Tally-Ho* off Penang on 11 January 1944.

▼
Tally-Ho's commanding officer, Lieutenant-Commander L. W. A. Bennington. The photograph was taken in Bennington's previous command, the minelayer HMS *Porpoise*.

Malaya and the island of Sumatra. The new arrivals lost no time in making their presence felt. *Taurus* (Lieutenant-Commander M. R. G. Wingfield) sank the Japanese submarine *I34* on 12 November 1943. The Japanese submarine had been damaged in an earlier air attack and was bound for Penang when sunk in a snap attack. The Malacca Straits was a very productive area for submarine sinkings: a truly representative collection of two Japanese, one German and one ex-Italian boat under German command being sunk by T boats. Further sinkings were: the German *UIT23* (ex-Italian *Reginaldo Giuliani*) by *Tally-Ho* (Lieutenant-Commander L. W. A. Bennington) on 15 February 1944; the Japanese *I166* by *Telemachus* (Lieutenant-Commander W. King) on 17 July 1944 and the German *U859* by *Trenchant* (Lieutenant-Commander A. R. Hezlet) on 23 September 1944.

Successes were also obtained against other Japanese naval units. *Tally Ho* (Lieutenant-Commander L. W. A. Bennington) disposed of the 5,500-ton Japanese *Kuma* on 11 January 1944 off Penang. Bennington had sighted the cruiser exercising off Penang on 9 January and resolved to stay in the area in case the cruiser made another appearance. On the 11th she was sighted again with a destroyer and air escort: Bennington fired seven torpedoes from 1,900 yards with a 95° track angle, scoring two hits. The destroyer dropped eighteen depth-charges, two of which 'rattled the rigging a bit',[1] but Bennington successfully avoided the attack by keeping inshore. The cruiser *Kitakami* was more fortunate when she was attacked by *Templar* (Lieutenant

D. J. Beckley) on 27 January 1944 in a night attack off Penang. Beckley fired all eight bow torpedoes at long range despite the presence of three destroyers and was rewarded with two hits. *Kitakami*'s crew were evidently well worked-up in damage control for the cruiser was able to return to Penang.

One encounter with a Japanese warship resulted in *Tally-Ho* (Lieutenant-Commander L. W. A. Bennington) sustaining fairly spectacular damage. On 24 February 1944 while on the surface at night, charging batteries in the Malacca Straits, she sighted an enemy patrol vessel astern of her, subsequently identified as an escort of the *Hyabusa* class. The Japanese vessel crossed *Tally-Ho*'s stern from starboard to port and then turned in to ram. *Tally-Ho* went hard a starboard and the escort tore along the port side gouging out great lumps from the submarine's saddle tanks with her screw. While the Japanese vessel made off, evidently having sustained some damage, *Tally Ho* assumed a 15° list to port but was able to dive. The list was reduced to 12° by flooding O and Q starboard tanks and blowing Q port tank. *Tally-Ho* was able to return to Ceylon at about 10 knots although it was possible she might do an involuntary dive at any moment. Once she was docked at Colombo the extent of the damage was clear to all . . . 'Just like a tuddy toast rack' was one observer's comment.[2]

Not all actions against Japanese warships were with the torpedo. T-boat commanders quickly realized that the Japanese submarine-chasers were poorly armed: *Tally-Ho*, rather than submit to a depth-charging in shallow water, surfaced and demolished Submarine Chaser No. 2 in a gun action on 6 October 1944 in the Malacca Straits, scoring five hits in nineteen rounds. Indeed, there were few targets in this area worth a torpedo and T boats began to operate more as submersible gunboats than as submarines.

Operations in the Malacca Straits were an opportunity for T boats to use their minelaying capability which had not been demonstrated in either Home Waters or the Mediterranean. *Trespasser, Taurus, Tally-Ho, Tactician, Tantalus, Templar, Tantivy, Truculent, Trenchant, Tudor, Tradewind, Thorough* and *Thule* carried out fifteen minelays all in the Malacca Straits or off Sumatra: *Taurus* (Lieutenant-Commander M. R. G. Wingfield) and *Thorough* (Lieutenant-Commander R. G. Hopkins) undertaking two operations and the others one. All the lays were of 12 M Mk II tube-laid mines

▲
HMS *Templar* comes alongside at Colombo on 12 February 1944 having damaged the cruiser *Kitakami* on 27 January 1944. (IWM A.22500)

◄
HMS *Tally-Ho* in dry dock at Colombo, showing the damage received in her encounter with a *Hyabusa*-class escort on 24 February 1944.

except *Tudor*'s (Lieutenant S. A. Porter) which managed to lay only ten of her mines due to bad weather. The lays were carried out often under very difficult conditions close to land and *Truculent* (Lieutenant-Commander R. L. Alexander) and *Tally-Ho* (Commander L. W. A. Bennington) both grounded while laying their mines. For the record *Thorough* achieved the quickest minelay of the war, laying twelve mines, including two reloads, in 56 minutes during S/M MLO.21 on 23 December 1944 off Terutuan, north of Penang. The results of this campaign were not spectacular: one merchant ship *Kasumi Maru* sunk on 12 May 1944 in *Trespasser*'s field, another, *Nichioku Maru*, damaged in *Tally-Ho*'s field on 18 May 1944, and a submarine damaged, the Japanese *I.37*, in *Taurus*'s second field on 27 April 1944. However, although the successes were meagre, the minelaying campaign undoubtedly provided the Japanese with another problem and succeeded in forcing the Germans to abandon their U-boat base at Penang and move to Batavia.[3]

Another aspect of T-boat activities in the Far East was one or more boats operating together. These were in no sense 'Wolf-Packs' like those used by the U-boats in the Atlantic since British submarines lacked effective TBS equipment, but they were effective none the less. *Terrapin* (Lieutenant R. H. Brunner) and *Trenchant* (Commander A. R. Hezlet) worked the Malacca Straits together from 22 December 1944 to 4 January 1945 and sank two coasters and a trawler. A further three coasters were driven ashore by gunfire. Both submarines were out again from 24 February until 16 March 1945. The highlight of this joint patrol was the sinking by gunfire of Special Submarine Chaser No. 5 on 4 March 1945.

By the end of August 1944 there were 26 submarines in the Eastern Fleet, ten of which were T boats: *Zwaardvis*, *Telemachus*, *Tantivy* and *Tantalus* with the 8th Flotilla based on the depot ship *Maidstone* and *Terrapin*, *Trenchant*, *Tradewind*, *Tally-Ho*, *Tudor*, *Thorough* and

Thule with the 4th Flotilla based on the depot ship *Adamant*. This was more than could be usefully employed off the Malayan coast so the 8th Flotilla moved to Western Australia in August 1944 to operate in the South China Sea under the command of the US Commander, South West Pacific. The 4th Flotilla temporarily remained at Trincomalee while three short-ranged T-class submarines, *Thrasher*, *Torbay* and *Trident*, remained with the 2nd Flotilla at Ceylon.

In April 1945 *Adamant* and the 4th Flotilla also arrived at Fremantle and there was a reorganization of British submarines in the theatre. *Maidstone* was to move up to Subic Bay in the Philippines with the S-class submarines while *Adamant* remained at Fremantle with nine T boats: *Thorough*, *Tudor*, *Thule*, *Trenchant*, *Terrapin*, *Tradewind*, *Taciturn*, *Trump* and *Tiptoe*. The last three replaced *Tally-Ho*, *Telemachus*, *Tantivy* and *Tantalus* which had returned to the UK. A further eight T-class submarines were under orders to leave the UK with the depot ship *Aorangi*. Working from Fremantle meant a long passage up the west coast of Australia with a stand-off at Exmouth Bay to refuel before proceeding through the heavily defended Lombok Strait to their patrol areas. Passage of the Lombok Strait, where surface currents could reach seven knots, presented a formidable obstacle to T boats with their low surface speed. Matters were not improved when the Japanese strengthened the defences and patrols at the end of 1944 so that the nearby Ombai Strait or Timor Sea routes had to be used.

Unlike operations off Malaya, those in the SW Pacific area were governed by a number of restrictions. Attacks on other submarines were permitted only if the target were positively identified as hostile because of the large number of US boats operating in the same area. Likewise restrictions were imposed, though lifted in July 1945, on attacks in the Lombok and Karimata Straits to avoid disclosing the extent to which Allied submarines were using these routes. The most difficult restriction concerned the prohibition of attacks on

► The 535GRT *Hyoshi Maru* burning after being shelled by *Tantalus* in the Malacca Straits on 10 June 1944. This target was typical of those found in waters off the Malayan coast. (Vice-Admiral Sir Hugh Mackenzie)

native craft in the Netherlands East Indies. In the
Malacca Straits commanding officers had complete
freedom to sink all shipping. Operational orders for the
SW Pacific stated that 'the gunning of small native craft
in the Netherlands East Indies or Philippine Islands
does the enemy little or no harm . . . we are not at war
with the natives of the Netherlands East Indies'.[4] In
practice this meant that the identity of a vessel had to
be established by boarding-party before it could be
sunk. The perils of stopping to search such craft are
evident: *Trenchant*'s boarding officer came face to face
with armed Japanese soldiers when he entered the
hold of a schooner which had been stopped in the

Celebes on 13 July 1945. The Japanese opened fire
upwards through the deck, so *Trenchant* lay off and
sank the schooner by gunfire.[5]

The first T boat to proceed on patrol from Fremantle
was *Telemachus* (Lieutenant-Commander W. King), but
it was the Dutch *Zwaardvis* (Lieutenant-Commander H.
A. W. Goossens) which was the first to come to grips
with the Japanese in this theatre. In his first patrol
from 26 September to 26 October 1944, Goossens sank
U168 on 6 October off Surabaya and followed this up
with the sinking of the minelayer *Itsukushima* on 17
October: an auxiliary minelayer was also damaged in
this attack. For this patrol Goossens was awarded the

► Rear-Admiral Hendrikus Goossens, wartime commander of the Dutch submarine *Zwaardvis*. The photograph was taken in 1960 when Goossens was Flag Officer Sea Training. (Royal Netherlands Navy)

Militaire Willems-Orde, the highest Dutch award for gallantry. The citation commented on his 'great courage, skill and perseverance . . . not withstanding heavy opposition'. Goossens had escaped to England in 1940 and had commanded the submarines *O.9* and *O.14* before commissioning *Zwaardvis* on 13 November 1943. He remained in command for another three patrols in the SW Pacific before being relieved by his First Lieutenant, Lt. J. van Dapperen, on grounds of ill health.[6]

Opportunities for action against major Japanese naval units were uncommon in this theatre since the crippling fuel shortage was drastically restricting the movements of the few surviving major Japanese warships. On 11 February 1945, east of the Anamba Islands, *Tantalus* (Lieutenant-Commander H. S. Mackenzie) had the last sighting of an enemy capital ship by a British submarine. The targets were the battleships *Ise* and *Hyuga* making their way back to Japan. When the unmistakable pagoda-like fighting tops came over the horizon, Mackenzie tried to get ahead of his targets: '. . . we were flogging along at full speed trying to gain bearing on them but just about holding our own, and one just hoped that maybe they would do a zig zag and turn towards us and we could dive and get in an attack. We were about 60–70 degrees on their port bow. They were surrounded by an absolute swarm of aircraft like bees around a hive, and suddenly one of them detached itself and headed in our direction so we then decided to dive and that put paid to it.'[7] It was this patrol, from 3 January to 26 February 1945, that was the longest undertaken by a British submarine during the Second World War: 55 days and covering 11,692 nautical miles. *Tantalus* returned to Fremantle with less

than 5 per cent of her fuel remaining since she had been unable to refuel at Exmouth Gulf on the return journey.[8] In doing so, Mackenzie broke his own record for his previous patrol, from 16 October to 6 December 1944, in which he had spent 52 days at sea and travelled 11,539 nautical miles.

One Japanese warship which did not get away was the cruiser *Asigara* (10,000 tons, eight 8-inch guns) sunk on 8 June 1945 by *Trenchant* (Commander A. R. Hezlet). Acting on information supplied by the US submarine *Chubb* that a *Nachi*-class cruiser had been sighted entering Batavia, Hezlet requested permission to remain on patrol at the northern end of the Banka Strait. *Trenchant*'s OOW sighted *Asigara*'s masts through the periscope at 1148 at a range of 12,000 yards. Hezlet could not improve his firing position to more than 4,000 yards off track and during the 21 minutes before the DA came on he made his calculations with considerable precision. A full bow salvo of eight tubes was fired at 1209, individually aimed from a quarter of a length ahead to a quarter length astern. To avoid broaching, speed was increased after firing and the forward trim and Q tanks were flooded and correct depth was held within four feet. The torpedo tracks must have been clearly visible to *Asigara*'s lookouts, but the cruiser could not alter course to port to avoid the torpedoes because of the shoreline and was thus forced to alter to starboard: the worst possible option with torpedoes approaching from just abaft the starboard beam. At 1212 the first torpedo hit abreast Y turret followed by four more hits along the length of the ship: when the smoke cleared she was observed stopping with a list to starboard, her bows blown off and a heavy fire raging forward. Some thirty members

▲◀
Lieutenant-Commander H. S. Mackenzie, commanding officer of HMS *Tantalus* (above), which completed the two longest patrols carried out by a British submarine during the war. The photograph was taken in 1942 when Mackenzie was commanding officer of *Thrasher*. (IWM A.10254/ FL.7063)

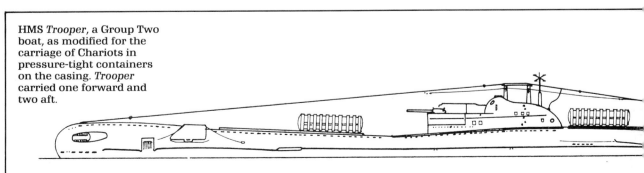

HMS *Trooper*, a Group Two boat, as modified for the carriage of Chariots in pressure-tight containers on the casing. *Trooper* carried one forward and two aft.

▲
The Japanese cruiser
Asigara at the Coronation
Naval Review at Spithead
in May 1937. She was sunk
by *Trenchant* on 8 June
1945. (IWM DS.595/34)

▶
HMS *Trenchant* returns to
Fremantle in June 1945
after the sinking of
Asigara. (IWM A.30366)

of *Trenchant*'s crew were able to watch *Asigara*'s last moments through the search periscope. When Hezlet retrieved his periscope, by going to the back of the queue, he fired a further two torpedoes which missed. Meanwhile his periscope attracted some retaliatory fire from *Asigara*'s AA armament which was hardly surprising since about 8 feet of the search periscope had been up with the submarine turning at 5 knots. Eventually *Asigara* was seen to capsize in great clouds of steam and smoke.[9]

No T boats were lost in the Far East though *Terrapin* (Lieutenant R. H. Brunner) was so badly damaged that she was beyond repair. On 19 May 1945 Brunner had attacked a small tanker escorted by a frigate and after firing ordered the submarine to 60 feet, but *Terrapin* struck the bottom with 57 feet showing on the depth gauge. For the next five hours she was subjected to an intense depth-charge attack, but the submarine survived and surfaced shortly after dark. The frigate was only 5,000 yards away but did not sight the submarine. *Terrapin*, however, was in a mess with her W/T and gyro broken and 80 per cent of depth and pressure gauges smashed. More seriously the depth-charges had 'dished in' the pressure hull to a maximum depth of 1 foot 3 inches between frames 15 to 25 on the port side, crushing the Main Line and displacing the WRT and AIV tanks. *Terrapin* was able to dive, but the hull leaked badly and she faced a long passage back to Fremantle on the surface. On 21 May help appeared in the form of the US submarine *Cavalla* (Lieutenant-Commander E. J. Kossler, USN). Kossler ordered extra lookouts and close-range armament to *Cavalla*'s bridge

and announced he would escort her to Fremantle. His announcement that '. . . in the event of enemy contact we will remain on the surface. We will not dive' is still remembered with gratitude by *Terrapin*'s crew.[10]

The combined patrols which had proved so successful in the Malacca Straits were continued in the SW Pacific. *Tiptoe*'s and *Trump*'s activities have already been referred to in Chapter 4. *Thorough* (Lieutenant-Commander A. G. Chandler, RNR) and *Taciturn* (Lieutenant-Commander E. T. Stanley) together rolled up a Japanese convoy on 16 June 1945 off Surabaya, consisting of an armed trawler, an old Dutch submarine, and a submarine-chaser towing a large hulk. *Taciturn* disposed of the submarine-chaser, the submarine and the hulk, firing 205 rounds of 4 inch. She then drove the trawler towards *Thorough* which surfaced and sank her.[11] It fell to *Tiptoe* (Lieutenant R. L. Jay) to fire the last British torpedo of the war on 3 August in a joint attack on a convoy with *Trump* (Lieutenant A. A. Catlow). *Thorough* was the last British submarine to be attacked, being bombed in the Lombok Strait the day after the war officially ended.

Wherever they operated, T boats were called upon for a variety of Special Operations. Some of these operations were against specific military objectives, but the majority were in support of the Special Operations Executive (SOE) and, in the Far East, the US Office of Strategic Services (OSS). The operations against purely military targets involved T boats supporting X-craft midget submarines, the two-man 'Chariots' and landing/retrieving parties of commandos for raids on specific objectives.

X-craft were midget submarines armed with two ½-ton explosive charges, and had been designed with the aim of crippling the 'Beast', Churchill's name for the German battleship *Tirpitz*. T-class submarines took part in only one X-craft operation, but it was undoubtedly the most famous of all: Operation 'Source'; an attack on *Tirpitz* by six X-craft in September 1944. Six submarines were to participate in this operation including two T class: *Truculent* (Lieutenant R. L. Alexander) and *Thrasher* (Lieutenant A. R. Hezlet). They were fitted with a towing bar on the port side of the after casing by the No. 11 torpedo tube to enable them to tow the X-craft to a position off the Norwegian coast from where the midgets would proceed independently. At 1600 on 11 September 1943, *Truculent* left Loch Cairnbawn towing *X.6* (Lieutenant Donald Cameron, RNR) followed by *Thrasher* towing *X.5* (Lieutenant H. Henty-Creer, RNVR). Neither *Truculent*'s nor *Thrasher*'s X-craft returned: *X.6* was detected, but managed to leave both charges under *Tirpitz* before Cameron and his crew were captured. Of the fate of Henty-Creer's *X.5* little is known. She was last sighted on 20 September by *X.7*. The Germans claimed to have sunk a midget, which may have been *X.5*, on 22 September and later found wreckage but no personal effects.[12]

The 'Chariot' was another weapon with which T boats were involved. A two-man craft, rather like a

HMS *Terrapin*, the only T class to be seriously damaged in the Far East, at Barrow in January 1944 on completion. (IWM FL.3524)

Detailed photograph showing *Terrapin*'s hull 'dished in' below the port forward hydroplane, which has been removed to facilitate repairs. (Royal Navy Submarine Museum)

▼
Commander A. R. Hezlet watching *Trenchant*'s shells falling around Special Minesweeper No. 105 in the Lombok Strait on 24 May 1945. (IWM HU.51761 Jim Gilbert)

▲
HMS *Thrasher* towing X.5 out of Loch Cairnbawn on 11 September 1943 to begin the long journey across the North Sea before the attack on *Tirpitz*. (Royal Navy Submarine Museum)

◄
HMS *Trooper* alongside the depot ship *Titania* in 1942, showing the two pressure-tight containers on her after casing in which chariots were carried. In both cases the chariots have been withdrawn for inspection. (Royal Navy Submarine Museum)

torpedo with a detachable warhead, the Chariot, or 'Jeep', was carried in a cylindrical container mounted on top of the submarine's casing. The containers were ungainly structures which gave the submarine a large silhouette, made them unhandy while diving and detracted from their seaworthiness. To launch the chariot, the submarine would surface and the chariots would be pulled out of the containers, the 'charioteers' would climb on to their 'mounts' and the submarine would then trim down until the chariot floated clear.

After the failure of an operation using chariots in Norway in October 1942, it was decided that they would be better employed in the Mediterranean. Accordingly three T boats. *Trooper* (Lieutenant J. S. Wraith), *P.311* (Lieutenant R. D. Cayley) and *Thunderbolt* (Lieutenant-Commander C. B. Crouch) were fitted with containers on their casings in which the chariots would be carried. *P.311* and *Thunderbolt* each carried two chariots, one forward and one aft of the conning tower, but *Trooper* carried two aft, side by side on the casing between the two external torpedo tubes, and one forward.

Operation 'Principal' was the code-name for an attack on the Italian battle fleet at Taranto, but alternative targets had to be chosen when the Italian fleet moved to Naples. *Trooper* and *Thunderbolt*'s chariots

were to attack merchant shipping and a new cruiser at Palermo, while *P.311* went after two 8-inch gun cruisers at La Maddalena in Northern Sardinia. On the night of 2/3 January *Trooper* and *Thunderbolt* launched five chariots off Palermo, three of which ran into trouble and had to abandon their attack. The other two chariots: XXII (Lieutenant R. T. G. Greenland and Leading Signalman A. Ferrier); and XVI (Sub-Lieutenant R. G. Dove and Leading Seaman J. Freel) did tremendous damage. The 8,500-ton liner *Viminale* was damaged beyond repair and the new cruiser *Ulpio Traiano* sank at her moorings.

What of Cayley's *P.311*? Because the passage of the Sicillian Channel was considered to be as dangerous as the operation itself, *Trooper* and *Thunderbolt* were held back until Cayley had reported he was safely through. His signal was received at 0130 on 31 December, giving his position as 38°10'N,11°30'W, and this was the last heard from *P.311*. There is no evidence that she ever launched her chariots and it is most likely that she was mined in the approaches to Maddalena.

The overall success of Operation 'Principal' must be doubtful. The Italians lost a new cruiser and had a valuable troopship damaged, but *P.311*, her crew and charioteers were lost, together with HMS *Traveller*

(Lieutenant-Commander D. St. Clair Ford), mined while engaging in a reconnaissance of Taranto harbour on or about 4 December, before the operation. Furthermore, as the Naval Staff History has it: '. . . the diversion of submarines for chariot-carrying and recovery duties gravely interrupted their normal patrol activities at a time when there were many valuable targets at sea on the Axis supply routes to North Africa'.[13]

Thunderbolt conducted one more chariot operation in the Mediterranean. On 18 January 1943 she launched two chariots in an attack on Tripoli harbour to prevent the Axis blocking the harbour, since the town was expected to fall to the Eighth Army within days.

One further chariot attack was carried out using a T boat; this was in the Far East against two Italian liners, *Sumatra* of 4,859 tons and *Volpi* of 5,292 tons, which were lying at Puket, north of Penang. The chariots were successfully launched from *Trenchant* (Lieutenant-Commander A. R. Hezlet) on the night of 27 October 1944, *Sumatra* was sunk and *Volpi* damaged. The chariots then made their way back to *Trenchant* and safety. This was the most successful chariot operation: two valuable transports had been denied the enemy with no losses among the charioteers or 'parent' submarine. No further chariot operations were carried out in the Far East for the Admiralty considered that: '. . . although targets exist, they do not afford that reasonable prospect of escape for charioteers which is essential when dealing with an inhuman enemy'.[14]

Commando operations were another aspect of special operations in which T boats played a part. The best known was Operation 'Frankton': a raid carried out by twelve Royal Marine Commandos under the command of Major Haslar in December 1942 against a blockade-runner lying at Bordeaux. The commandos were equipped with folding, two-man canoes, known as Folboats, and a large number of explosive charges, and were conveyed to a position just off the Gironde estuary by *Tuna* (Lieutenant R. P. Raikes). *Tuna* reached her position on 7 December and in the evening surfaced to launch the canoes. The raid, immortalized in the film *Cockleshell Heroes*, was a success with four merchant ships being badly damaged.

Triumph (Lieutenant-Commander W. J. Woods) took part in a less successful operation in April 1941. Operation 'Colossus', the first parachute operation undertaken by the British Army, had the apparent object of inflicting endemic diarrhoea on the inhabitants of Brindisi by blowing up an aqueduct carrying their water supply from the Appenines. The operation was partially successful in that a railway line was blown up and the water supply disrupted, but the paratroops failed to topple the aqueduct because its supports were of concrete and not masonry as supposed. *Triumph* was scheduled to collect the paratroops from the south bank of the River Sele, but Commander G. W. 'Shrimp' Simpson, senior submarine officer at Malta, considered that the rendezvous position was compromised after a Whitley aircraft engaged in the operation had crashed. *Triumph* was ordered to sail for the pick-up, but was later recalled after Simpson signalled the Admiralty of his concern.[15] Sadly the paratroops were captured and became prisoners of war.

Torbay (Lieutenant-Commander A. C. C. Miers) and *Talisman* (Lieutenant-Commander M. Willmott) landed commandos west of Apollonia on the North African coast with the object of killing or capturing General Rommel whose headquarters were thought to be at Beda Littoria. The commandos were landed on 14 November 1941. *Torbay*'s party were landed successfully, but *Talisman* had difficulties due to deteriorating weather and not all her party got ashore. Miers chose to make the pick-up along and ordered *Talisman* back to Alexandria. The raid was a failure, Intelligence having been completely wrong, and only three of the commandos returned to Cairo, but overland instead of in *Torbay*. *Torbay*'s first attempt to collect the three on 18 November was frustrated by bad weather and, having agreed to return the next night, Miers withdrew. During the course of 19 November, the three commandos were discovered and split up. When *Torbay* returned to the beach it was deserted. Accordingly Miers moved to the secondary beach, but again found it deserted so returned to Alexandria. Miers was justifiably furious when he later discovered that some of the commandos had made a private arrangement with *Talisman* for a third pick-up point about which he knew nothing.[16]

The majority of Special Operations involved T boats in the landing/recovery of agents. The case for using a submarine in this kind of work was nicely balanced. The submarine could, literally, disappear after the operation and was almost undetectable. On the other hand submarines were valuable units of the fleet and could not be lightly risked in operations that had limited military objectives. Lastly, there was the ever-present risk that treachery might lead to the landing site/pick-up point being compromised, in which case a submarine and her crew could be lost.

Talisman (Lieutenant-Commander P. S. Francis) was the first T boat to land agents: on 2 August 1941 she landed two agents by the Hourtin Light near the Gironde estuary. Landing operations were not common in Home Waters where the air route was quicker and where SOE had their own 'private navy' and were not beholden to the Admiralty. In the Mediterranean there was more scope for this sort of work following the German invasion of Yugoslavia, Greece and Crete. *Triumph*, *Taku*, *Tetrarch*, *Truant*, *Talisman*, *Thunderbolt*, *Thorn*, *Turbulent*, *Thrasher* and *Tribune* all took part in landing and recovering agents.

But it was in the Far East that landing operations came into their own. Until long-range aircraft became available submarines constituted the only means of inserting special forces into SE Asia. The Navy reluctantly approved these missions, but usually only as part of a routine patrol: it was a compromise that was

HMS *Talisman* in February 1942 on her return to the UK for a refit. Her 'Jolly Roger' has one dagger embroidered for special operations. By the time this photograph was taken *Talisman* had completed two such operations: the landing of agents in France in August 1941 followed by the abortive raid on Rommel's HQ in November 1941. (IWM AD No. 7470)

A weatherbeaten *Truant* goes 'around the buoy' for the benefit of the Press in Holy Loch on 3 December 1942 following her return to the UK in November. *Truant* was the only British submarine to sink enemy ships in all three theatres of operations. (IWM A.13147)

deeply unsatisfactory. From January 1944 to the end of the war T boats carried out 77 patrols from Ceylon of which 43 involved a special operation. The Fremantle-based boats spent less time on special operations: of nineteen patrols carried out by T boats from September 1944 until the end of the war, only two involved a special operation. Most of the operations required the landing of single or a small group of agents but the record for quantity carried must go to *Thule* (Lieutenant-Commander A. C. G. Mars). On 6 February 1945 she had landed 4,000lb of stores for an SOE group on Johore, north of Singapore. On 25 May she was back again with 8,000lb of stores, three officers and sixteen Royal Marines. In order to land all the gear *Thule* embarked fourteen LCRs and eleven outboard engines which meant she sailed without any reload torpedoes.

Special operations were unpopular particularly those where the submarine had to refrain from offensive operations against the enemy for fear of compromising the landing/recovery. Thus on 2 May 1944, *Templar* (Lieutenant T. G. Ridgeway) had to let an unescorted 3,000-ton merchant ship – a rare target in the Malacca

Straits – pass unhindered because he was engaged in transporting an SOE reconnaissance party. The incident caused Captain S4, Captain H. M. C. Ionides, to comment, 'another case of a target lost because of a special operation'.[17] A sense of dissatisfaction at the number of special operations required was not ameliorated by the impression of little co-ordination between the various Intelligence bodies. Thus *Tally Ho* (Lieutenant-Commander L. W. A. Bennington) found herself embarking two parties from two different organizations, SOE and the ISLD (Inter Services Liaison Department: the Far Eastern manifestation of SIS, better known as MI.6). Disagreements between the two organizations onboard resulted in the SOE officer vetoing the landing of the ISLD party despite the fact that Bennington considered the landing quite safe.[18] But the fact is that by 1945 there were so few targets left for British submarines in the Far East – particularly off Malaya – that special operations constituted their only viable employment. Japan's merchant marine had been decimated and there was, literally, nothing left to sink.

8. The Admiralty Regrets

Construction of the T class coincided with a radical review of submarine escape policy conducted by the Admiralty following the loss of HMS/M *Poseidon* on 9 June 1931 and HMS/M *M.2* on 26 January 1932. Hitherto Admiralty policy with regard to submarine escape had been non-existent or at best confused. Submariners were provided with the means to escape, notably the Davis Submarine Escape Apparatus (DSEA), and submarines were fitted with escape hatches, but policy was that submariners should wait until help arrived rather than rely upon their own efforts.

Eight men had escaped from *Poseidon* in June 1931, carrying out a 'Compartment Escape' from a depth of 125 feet thus demonstrating that escape from a sunken submarine was possible. In March 1934 the First Lord of the Admiralty announced the new policy in a statement to the House of Commons.[1] Henceforth, submariners should not wait for rescue but rely on the DSEA together with their own courage and initiative. Escape trunks or 'Twill Trunks' were to be fitted to existing submarines and greater emphasis was to be placed on training, with escape tanks being built at Gosport, Malta and Hong Kong. Compartment Escape was to become the accepted method for leaving a sunken submarine throughout the 1930s. The procedure was as follows: the Twill Trunk was lowered to the level required by the depth of water in which the submarine was lying, and lashed down to special eyeplates on the deck. The bulkhead doors were shut, all the survivors being concentrated in one compartment. The flood valves were opened and the compartment flooded-up. While this was in progress the men breathed using their DSEA sets. When pressure was equalized it was shown on a differential pressure gauge. A rating then ducked under the trunk and climbed the ladder to open a vent in the upper hatch to release the air trapped in the trunk which then flooded forming a 'column of water' within the compartment. He then released the clips on the hatch and opened it. Each man then ducked under the trunk in turn and went up.

The DSEA set, in service since 1929, worked on the 'closed cycle' breathing system and consisted of a high-pressure cylinder containing thirty minutes' supply of oxygen from the cylinder into the breathing bag, inhaling through a mouthpiece. He exhaled CO_2 which was diverted through a valve in the mouthpiece to a cylinder containing a purifying agent, soda lime, before being returned to the breathing-bag. Each set came complete with goggles, a nose clip – to prevent the wearer breathing through his nose – and an apron or drogue to allow the wearer to check his ascent on the way up, thus avoiding lung damage caused by rapid changes of pressure. DSEA sets were kept in sealed lockers which took up a considerable amount of room. In November 1934, the Director of Plans, Captain E. L. S. King, MVO, considered that: '. . . DSEA should not be carried in wartime. The availability of such gear is calculated to precipitate a panic during a depth-charge attack. If there is no escape apparatus, each man will know that his only chance in danger is to do his work and obey orders.'[2] This was an astonishing statement from one who had not served in submarines and, needless to say, his suggestion was curtly rejected by Rear-Admiral (Submarines), Rear-Admiral Noel Laurence.

But something more than improved training in the use of the DSEA and the fitting of Twill Trunks was needed. The new submarines of the T class were to be fitted with two-man escape chambers: one forward between the torpedo stowage compartment and the seamen's messdeck, and the other aft between the motor room and the stokers' messdeck. There was some resistance to the idea of special escape chambers since they involved fitting extra hatches in the pressure hull with the attendant risks of damage under depth-charge attack. The Staff had wanted to incorporate the forward chamber in the torpedo stowage compartment and the after chamber in the engine room, or failing that in Z tank, but these plans proved impractical. Each chamber was a cylindrical structure built integrally with the forward and after escape bulkheads. Circular, quick-acting doors allowed access from either side although a separate bulkhead door was fitted allowing the escape chamber to be 'by-passed'. Two sets of controls were provided so that the chamber could be operated from whatever side remained unflooded: a third set of controls was fitted inside so that the last man to leave the submarine could work the chamber. The procedure for working the escape chamber was as follows. After two men, wearing their DSEA sets, had entered the chamber, the access door was clipped shut behind them. The screw clips on the upper hatch were then released so that the hatch was held shut by sea pressure and the external 'toe clip'. The clutch on the upper hatch operating gear was then freed so that the hatch could be pushed open once the 'toe clip' had been released. Sea-water was then admitted through a flood valve and the air in the

◄
Instruction in the use of the DSEA set. The instructor is adjusting the flow of oxygen from the cylinder at the bottom of the set. The rolled up canvas at the front of the set is the drogue used to check the man's ascent. (IWM A.29501)

◄◄
Early escape training in the 15-foot deep escape tank at Fort Blockhouse: the trainee, wearing a Davis Submarine Escape Apparatus, is beginning his ascent to the surface. The artificiality of such training is apparent.

▼
HMS *Tribune*'s after escape chamber seen looking aft from the motor room. Beneath the open door to the chamber are sealed lockers containing DSEA sets. On the outside of the door are clipped two watertight torches; instructions for using the chamber are given on the brass plate between the torches. (IWM A.10930)

chamber vented outboard, no attempt being made to retain an airlock. The external 'toe clip' was released once the chamber had flooded, the men pushed open the hatch and swam up to the surface. Those remaining inside the submarine could see when the chamber was clear by watching through special glass ports. They then shut the upper hatch by engaging the clutch on the operating gear and replaced the 'toe clip'. The flood and vent valves were shut and the chamber drained down into the bilges. Once the chamber had drained down, the next two men could enter and repeat the process.

The combination of escape chamber and DSEA set seemed to offer those serving in the new T class an excellent chance of surviving an accident. Yet in June 1939 the Navy and the country were horrified by the loss of the brand-new *Thetis* in Liverpool Bay with 103 men onboard. As one observer recalled: 'Never will I forget the films and photographs of the stern of *Thetis* swinging in the tide of Liverpool Bay with men doomed to die so soon and yet so near to apparent help.'[3] *Thetis* (Lieutenant-Commander G. Bolus) was the first of the class, built by Cammell Laird at Birkenhead. By March 1939 she was ready to begin her trials. Her first diving trials in the Gareloch were postponed when the forward hydroplanes jammed, so her first dive was planned to take place in Liverpool Bay on 1 June 1939. In addition to her own complement of 53 officers and men, she was carrying an additional 50 people, most of whom were directly concerned with the trials. The largest single group of 'passengers' were the 26 Cammell Laird employees who were to work the machinery (the Navy having not yet officially accepted *Thetis*) under the direction of the submarine's officers. There were nine other naval officers aboard, four from *Trident* and *Taku*, also under construction at Cammell Laird, and five others concerned with the trials. There were four employees of Vickers Armstrong, one from Brown Bros & Co, two from City Caterers (Liverpool) Ltd – who provided the 'big eats' that were such a feature of these events – and a Mersey River pilot.[4]

At 1400 on 1 June, Bolus gave the order to dive, but *Thetis* was reluctant to submerge – even with all ballast and auxiliary tanks flooded and with the hydroplanes at 10° to dive. It was not unusual for a boat to be trimmed light for her first dive, so Bolus ordered a check to be made that *Thetis* was carrying all the water indicated on the trim statement. This involved checking whether or not Nos. 5 and 6 tubes were full. Since both tubes contained 1,600lb of water, the weight would make the difference between *Thetis* being able to dive or not.

Lieutenant Frederick Woods, the torpedo officer, went forward and used the test cock on each tube to check whether or not it was flooded. All proved empty except for No. 6 tube which was at least half-full. Unknown to Woods, the test cock of No. 5 tube door was blocked on the inside by enamel paint. Woods then decided to carry out an inspection of the interiors of all six tubes. He inspected the bow cap indicators, located

▲
HMS *Thetis* under way toward her test dive in Liverpool Bay on 1 June 1939. The photograph was taken at about 1300 hours from the Isle of Man steamer *Fanella* inbound for Liverpool and is the last photograph ever taken of the submarine. (George Luck)

▶
Wreckmaster Brock clings to *Thetis*'s steeply angled stern on the afternoon of 2 June as he vainly tries to unscrew the manhole cover leading through to Z tank.

between the two banks of tubes, to ensure that the bow caps were shut. He then asked Leading Seaman Hambrook, a senior torpedo rating, to check that the bow-cap operating levers were set to 'Shut' and received the report that they were.

Yet Woods' inspection of the bow-cap indicators was not as thorough as it should have been. When the submarine was salved the indicator for No. 5 tube was found set in the 'Open' position. Yet the fault does not lie entirely with Woods. Unbelievably the indicators were arranged one above the other in the order 1, 2, 3, 4, 6 and 5 so that the bottom indicator was for No. 5 tube. Moreover the indicator for No. 5 tube was obscured by a horizontal bar in front of it. Worse still, the 'Open' and 'Shut' positions were different on each indicator. On that for No. 5 tube 'Shut' was at five o'clock, but for the other tubes 'Shut' was at 11 o'clock. Woods probably looked down the row of indicators, saw that their pointers lined up and assumed that all was well.

Woods then ordered Hambrook to open up the tubes one by one and he inspected the first four without any problems. But when opening No. 5 tube, Hambrook reported that the lever was stiff. While he applied more weight to the lever, water began to spray out from behind the door and moments later the door was flung back and water began to flood into the tube space.

Immediately Bolus ordered main ballast to be blown to bring *Thetis* to the surface. Had the flooding confined itself to the tube space *Thetis* might have been brought to the surface safely. However, Woods and the torpedo party could not shut the watertight door in the bulkhead (there are four doors in this bulkhead: on this occasion three were clipped shut) between the tube space and the torpedo stowage compartment which had to be pulled 'up-hill' against the bow-down angle of the submarine. Their task was not aided in that the

door was fitted with eighteen separate turnbuckles, one of which was jammed. With water already flooding into the torpedo stowage compartment and the prospect of chlorine gas emissions should the water flow further aft and into the battery, Woods ordered everyone back behind the second watertight bulkhead, into the accommodation space. The watertight door in this bulkhead was secured by a quick-acting wheel which was rapidly secured.

Thetis bottomed in 150 feet with a 45° bow-down angle, but soon levelled off. Her situation was dire with two compartments flooded and twice the number of men onboard. Bolus decided to try to drain down the torpedo stowage compartment: with only one compartment flooded, *Thetis* could surface. The plan was for a man wearing a DSEA set, to enter the torpedo stowage compartment through the escape chamber, make his way forward and close the door in the watertight bulkhead between the tube space and torpedo stowage compartment. He would then open two main line suction valves and the ballast pumps would expel the water. Four members of *Thetis*'s crew showed great gallantry in attempting this hazardous operation, but each time had to give in, overcome by the pain caused by pressure on their ears as the escape chamber was flooded up. The plan was abandoned, but as the subsequent inquiry pointed out, it was doomed to failure since at that depth the ballast pumps could expel 70 tons per hour, but *Thetis* was flooding at a rate of 135 tons an hour.[5] Throughout the long night of 1 June, the men in *Thetis* struggled to raise the stern of the submarine until by morning some 18 feet of her stern stuck up above the surface of Liverpool Bay. But as the night wore on, the air became foul with a high concentration of CO_2 which induced a feeling of lassitude. The four men that escaped, remembered the effort it took to pull themselves up the engine room to

◀
The salvage vessel *Vigilant* closes *Thetis*'s stern in a last desperate bid to free those trapped inside the submarine. Moments after this photograph was taken *Thetis* slipped beneath the waves for the last time.

► The piece of bitumastic enamel removed from the inside of the rear door of No. 5 tube which blocked the test cock, rendering it useless.

►► The bow cap indicator of No. 5 tube showing the pointer set at the 'open' position.

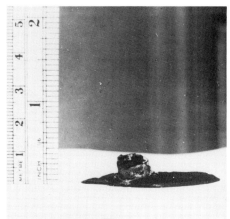

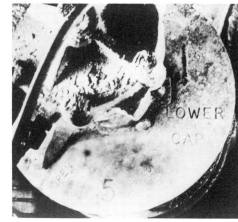

► *Thetis*'s fore-ends, after salvage, looking forward showing the two doors leading forward into the tube space. At the time of the accident the starboard door was closed, but it proved impossible to shut the port door and secure the eighteen turnbuckles against *Thetis*'s increasing bow down angle to stem the flow of water. The single clip at the top right side of the door was secured by *Thetis*'s TGM, Petty Officer E. Mitchell, who gallantly remained behind in this compartment until ordered to leave.

the escape chamber and how difficult it was to breathe.

Thetis had been provided with an escort for the dive, the tug *Grebecock*, in which were Lieutenant R. E. Coltart and a telegraphist for liaison purposes. Coltart had been concerned at the sudden way *Thetis* had disappeared and by her failure to carry out any of the pre-arranged exercises. But it was not until 1615 that he sent a deliberately innocuous signal inquiring about the length of *Thetis*'s dive, which he hoped would 'convey anxiety without raising alarm'.[6] Due to a chapter of misfortunes his signal was not received at Fort Blockhouse, Submarine Headquarters in Portsmouth, until 1815. Fortunately Blockhouse was already concerned about *Thetis*, having not received her surfacing report, and Coltart's signal prompted the ordering of a major search. At dawn on 2 June HMS *Brazen* (Lieutenant-Commander R. H. Mills), a destroyer *en route* for Devonport and diverted to the search, sighted the submarine's stern above the water. *Brazen* had, in fact, been searching all night, but her task had been complicated by false reports. No sooner had *Brazen* dropped explosive charges alongside *Thetis* to signal

her arrival, then two heads appeared in the water. The first two men had escaped and it looked as if all would be well.

Lieutenant-Commander Bolus had delayed ordering escapes until he was certain help was at hand, but the deteriorating conditions in the submarine forced him to proceed. The first two out were Captain H. P. Oram, commanding officer of 5th Submarine Flotilla which *Thetis* was to join, and Lieutenant Frederick Woods, the Torpedo Officer. Oram brought with him notes by *Thetis*'s Engineer Officer on how to salve the submarine which included the injunction to *Brazen* to keep 'constant watch for men escaping from after chamber'.[7] This injunction was to have a powerful effect on the rescuers.

Inside *Thetis*, morale went up at the sound of the explosive charges and with Oram and Wood's escape. At 1000 Leading Stoker Walter Arnold and Frank Shaw got out. Both men reported that conditions in the boat were dire and that unless something was done, the men in *Thetis* would be beyond help.

There were no more escapes from *Thetis* because the

◀ The salved *Thetis*, her periscope standards bent and buckled, on the beach at Moelfre Bay, Anglesey, for removal of the bodies and subsequent inspection by the members of the Tribunal. (IWM FL.2039)

▼ A memorial postcard issued to commemorate the tragedy. Stoker Walter Arnold's name erroneously appears in the second column, fourth from the top.

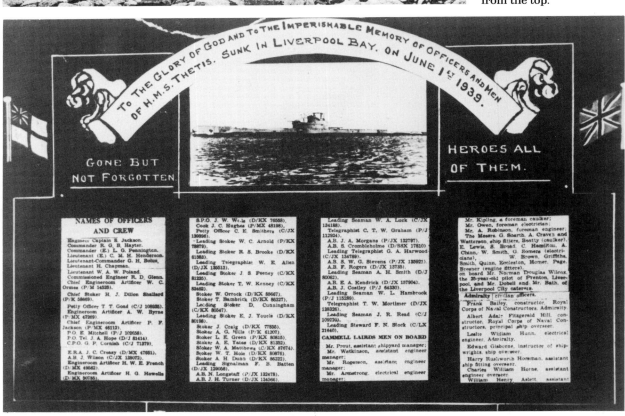

deadly effects of CO$_2$ poisoning had made themselves felt. After Arnold and Shaw's escape the rating working the chamber, exhausted and starved of oxygen, did not release the gearing on the upper hatch so that it could be opened from within: in effect the chamber was locked. Four more men tried to use the chamber, but were dragged out dead or dying having been unable to open the hatch. Sometime during the afternoon of 2 June, two more men entered the chamber and they too failed to open the hatch. But as they opened the door of the chamber to return to the motor room, they failed to turn off the flooding valve so that for the second time in two days, *Thetis* was once again open to the sea. The

inrush of water pushed up the dangerously high CO$_2$ level so that the ninety-nine men still alive were mercifully killed by the gas before the water had risen sufficiently to drown them.[8]

On the surface *Brazen*, joined by the salvage vessel *Vigilant* and a flotilla of *Tribal*-class destroyers, waited vainly for more men to appear. They were ever mindful of the warning to stay clear of the stern, although the precaution was taken of securing a wire from *Vigilant* to *Thetis*'s stern. But by the afternoon of 2 June, when no more men had appeared, it was decided to act. Wreckmaster Brock clambered up on to the stern to open a manhole cover leading into Z tank. Brock hoped to be able to pass through the tank into the steering machinery compartment. It was a bold plan, but as Brock unscrewed the nuts on the manhole cover, air began to escape violently and he shouted for instructions. He was told to carry on, but as he did so, *Thetis*'s stern began to twist violently in the tide and he was forced to abandon his attempt. At 1500 on 2 June desperation finally overrode any caution on the part of those on the surface. *Vigilant* came alongside *Thetis*'s stern intent on cutting a hole in her pressure hull. But the force of the tide now proved too strong for the wires securing the two vessels and at 1510 the cable parted and *Thetis* sank out of sight. It was all over and the operation became one of salvage rather than rescue.

The *Thetis* disaster shook the confidence of the Navy in the escape chamber/DSEA combination. Here was a submarine sunk in 150 feet and fitted with the latest equipment and yet fewer men had escaped than from *Poseidon*. Moreover the episode made the Admiralty consider whether the decision to abandon salvage as escape policy had been wise. A committee under the chairmanship of Admiral Sir Martin Dunbar-Nasmith[9] recommended the abolition of the two-man escape chambers and advocated a return to compartment escape although their report admitted that under certain circumstances the escape chambers had their advantages. An immediate consequence of the Nasmith report was that the escape chambers were no longer fitted in the T boats under construction. In practice this meant that only the Group One boats were built with the escape chambers which had held such promise. A more important modification was that, on 14 July 1939, Sir Stanley Goodall, Director of Naval Construction, ordered that the arrangement of bow-cap indicators was to be made consistent with 'Shut' at 10 o'clock and 'Open' at 2 o'clock, and that there were to be no obstructions in way of the indicators. Also, quick-acting doors were to be fitted throughout the submarine in place of those with the eighteen turnbuckles; the first boat to be so fitted was *Talisman*.[10]

Yet the escape chambers did not prove entirely redundant. In June 1943, HMS *Truant* carried out trials to see how practical it was for chariots to be launched from a submarine while the boat was bottomed. The 'charioteers' would leave the boat via the escape chambers, with their dressers, board their 'mounts' and proceed with their operation. The dresser would then return to the boat via the escape chamber. Thus the boat would not have to surface to launch chariots, thereby risking detection. It was an ingenious idea, but found to be impracticable. It did, however, pave the way for 'Exit/Re-entry' operations familiar to today's submariners.[11]

During the Second World War the study of escape techniques was not entirely neglected although for operational reasons submarines' escape hatches were usually bolted down from the outside to prevent them lifting under depth-charge attack. There were considerable advances in knowledge about CO_2 poisoning and

the correct use of the DSEA set. Despite the recommendations of the Nasmith Committee the idea of escape chambers did not completely die. The loss of HMS *Untamed* in May 1943 seemed to show that escape chambers were the only practicable means of escape: the crew had retreated to the engine room and begun to prepare for a compartment escape, but were overcome by CO_2 before they could get out.

Among those involved with the Inquiry into the loss of *Untamed* was Captain W. O. Shelford who had taken over escape training at Fort Blockhouse in 1941. Shelford noted that most submarines had two 'escape chambers' already fitted: the gun tower and the conning tower. Both had upper and lower lids and both could be modified to escape chambers without interfering with their normal use. Preliminary trials were carried out in HMS *Unbeaten* and found successful. Control of the upper hatch was achieved from within the control room by means of wires rove round a free-wheeling clutch hidden behind the conning tower ladder. However, Shelford thought something more substantial was required than a few flimsy wires so a rod gearing with a free-wheeling clutch was designed and fitted in HMS *Tribune*. Trials were carried out at Blyth in 1944 and despite an accident, which nearly cost the life of one of the divers testing the system, the conning tower escape arrangements were gradually introduced into all submarines. Procedure was as follows: before a man entered the conning tower those in the control room would check that the upper hatch gearing was in the idle position, that all electrical fittings in the tower except the light were isolated and that the vent cocks and drain valve were shut. Inside the tower the vent in the upper hatch would be ungagged and the vent valve would be checked to ensure that it was free. A man would then enter the tower closing the lower hatch behind him and commence breathing from BIBS, or TABS if fitted. He would then open the flood valves wide and when the water ceased to rise would vent the air by pulling down the hand lever of the vent. When the tower was flooded or nearly so, he would ease off the clips on the upper hatch and go up, taking care not to foul the periscope standards. Those in the control room, watching through the sighting port, having seen the escaper leave, would close the upper hatch using the hand-operated rod gearing, open the drain and vent valves and, once the tower was dry, the lower hatch. The upper hatch gearing would then be returned to the idle position and the next man would enter.[13] This route was well illustrated, although under somewhat idealized conditions, in the film *Morning Departure* which starred not only John Mills, but HMS *Tiptoe* as the ill-fated HMS *Trojan*.

After the Second World War a committee under the chairmanship of Captain Philip Ruck-Keene was formed to investigate all aspects of submarine escape and to profit from experience gained during the war. The Ruck-Keene report recommended that special one-

man escape chambers be adopted and that the DSEA set was also to be phased-out. Instead, men were to be trained in the technique of 'free ascent', coming to the surface without the aid of any breathing apparatus, from depths down to 100 feet. Such techniques had been witnessed by Ruck-Keene in the USA: all the escaper had to do was exhale hard on the way up to ensure that his lungs did not burst as the air trapped in them expanded. Finally, Ruck-Keene drove the last nail into the notion that submariners should wait for rescue before escaping. Calculations would have to be made showing how long the air would last: when the safe time expired an escape had to be made regardless of whether help was at hand. If such an escape were to be successful submariners had to be provided with the wherewithal to survive on the surface, possibly for some time and in very cold water before being rescued. Hence an immersion suit was required that would keep a man warm and dry and yet would be compact enough to be stowed in sufficient numbers within the submarine.

The Ruck-Keene Report was radical, but the 1940s were the age of 'austerity' and the recommendations would be expensive. The one-man chamber (OMEC) was ruled out after trials at HMS *Dolphin* on grounds of cost, and that it required considerable maintenance. In the absence of OMEC, a breathing system for use when flooding-up a compartment prior to escape, thus avoiding the twin perils of oxygen and CO_2 poisoning, was developed known as SEBA (Submarine Escape Breathing Apparatus), but was abandoned when it proved too bulky to stow in the required numbers. A new system called BIBS (Built In Breathing System) was designed to replace SEBA and consisted of large bottles of a 40 per cent oxygen and 60 per cent nitrogen mixture connected to a ring main running throughout the sub-

marine off which ran multiple outlets consisting of a tube and a mouthpiece: one for each member of the crew with one-third extra. BIBS was also extended to the conning tower in a system called TABS (Tower Air Breathing System) consisting of an air supply for two men.

Work proceeded slowly on other matters including the development of an immersion suit: a first model had been ready by the end of 1946, but by 1949 was only in limited production and not in general use throughout the fleet. None of the recommendations of the Ruck-Keene Report were implemented in the plans for the T Conversions or Streamlines, other than the provision of stowage for the immersion suits when they became available and the fitting of flooding and venting arrangements in the redesigned conning tower structure. It took another tragedy in which the name of a T-class submarine became linked with disaster to spur the authorities into doing something.

HMS *Truculent* (Lieutenant C. P. Bowers) was proceeding up the River Thames to Sheerness on the night of 12 January having spent the day carrying out post-refit trials. The OOW, Lieutenant J. N. Humphrey-Baker, observed the lights of what he took to be a stationary vessel on the north side of the channel. Bowers, called to the bridge by the OOW, agreed and ordered an alteration of course to port to clear the other ship. But the darkness of the night and the fact that the other vessel was wearing an additional red light indicating that she was carrying explosives deceived the two officers; the lights were those of the 543-ton Swedish tanker *Divina* proceeding downstream. *Truculent's* bows had just begun to swing on to the new course when *Divina's* loomed out of the darkness and crashed into the submarine's starboard side forward of the conning tower. Bowers and four other men on the

◄ HMS *Truculent* rammed
and sunk in the Thames
on 12 January 1950. The
photograph was taken in
May 1946: by the time
Truculent was sunk she
had been fitted with a
snort mast. (Wright and
Logan)

▲ *Truculent* after being
raised by the salvage
vessels *Ausdauer* and
Energie: she was
subsequently broken up at
Grays. (Royal Navy
Submarine Museum)

► Lieutenant C. P. Bowers,
commanding officer of
HMS *Truculent* and one of
fifteen survivors. (IWM
A.25133)

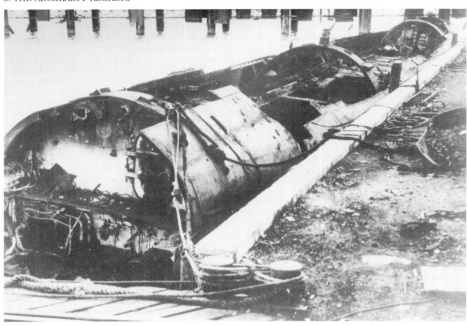

◄ The remains of *Truculent*, barely recognizable as a submarine being broken up at Grays in 1950. (Dr. Ian Buxton)

► HMS *Token* under way in 1961, showing the wooden fendering halfway along the forward casing to protect the BIBS cylinders.

bridge were thrown clear by the shock and it was nearly an hour before they were picked up by the Dutch ship *Almdyk*.

Inside the submarine ten men drowned in the flooding following the collision and the remaining sixty-four retreated to the engine room under the command of the First Lieutenant, F. J. Hindes. Hindes was familiar with the Ruck-Keene report and realized that there were too many men in the compartment for a successful escape to be carried out. Accordingly Hindes took one group into the after ends to escape from there while the remainder prepared to exit from the engine room under the command of the Chief ERA, Sam Hine. The sound of propellers overhead must have indicated to those in *Truculent* that rescue was at hand, and in both engine room and after ends the escape was carried out faultlessly despite there being insufficient DSEA sets to go round. Yet of the sixty-four men who escaped, only ten survived.[13]

The real tragedy of *Truculent* was that when the survivors reached the surface they found that they were entirely alone, with nothing but darkness and an ebbing tide that would carry most of them out to sea and certain death. The engine noises they had heard were those of routine river traffic. Among those who did not survive were Lieutenant Hindes and CERA Hine whose gallantry was recognized by the posthumous award of the Albert Medal: 'The splendid example set by Lieutenant Hindes and CERA Hine was beyond praise. Lieutenant Hindes by calm demeanour and clear orders maintained perfect discipline and was able to ensure that the greater part of those onboard moved safely to the engine room and the after end of the vessel . . . When all was ready he opened the escape hatch . . . and was not seen again. CERA Hine took

charge of the escape arrangements in the engine room. This duty he performed faultlessly.'[14]

The escapes had been carried out quickly because Hindes was well aware of the fate of those in *Thetis* and *Untamed* who had waited too long and been overcome by CO_2. With half the submarine flooded and an additional eighteen dockyard workers onboard, Hindes was quite correct in his fears. Moreover the submarine had sunk in an area crowded with shipping and that there had been a collision pre-supposed that the alarm would have been raised. Under the circumstances he could not do other than order a swift escape. The most damning aspect of the affair was that, having carried out a faultless escape, many of the men coming up without a DSEA set, fifty-four died on the surface by drowning or exposure through lack of suitable clothing: clothing which had been recommended nearly four years earlier. Such was the price of 'austerity'.

The *Truculent* disaster acted as a spur on the Navy to 'put its house in order' regarding escape. Production of immersion suits was accelerated and BIBS was fitted to all submarines though not necessarily throughout the boat. The cylinders containing the oxygen/nitrogen mixture were stowed between the pressure hull and the casing. Wooden fenders were built into the casing in way of these cylinders to protect them against a hit by a practice torpedo during exercises. By the end of the 1950s, the surviving T class had been thus fitted for escape:

1. BIBS fitted to all submarines.
2. A compartment at each end of the submarine containing an escape hatch, Twill Trunk, air purification equipment, quick-flooding valves and an outfit of immersion suits: one for each man onboard together with one-third extra.

▲ Members of *Telemachus's* ship's company try out their immersion suits in the harbour at Sydney in the early 1950s. Provision of such suits would have undoubtedly saved more lives in the *Truculent* disaster.

▼ A sailor inhales from the BIBS connection before going up through the Twill Trunk in a compartment escape.

▲ Wearing an immersion suit, Petty Officer L. Stokes prepares to enter *Tiptoe's* conning tower in October 1962 during escape trials off Malta. Lieutenant-Commander L. D. Hamlyn, Submarine Command Escape Officer, watches from beside the ladder.

▼ The ill-fated *Dakar* leaving Portsmouth in November 1967 before sailing for Israel. After calling at Gibraltar, she was never seen again. Note the very large fin containing a five-man exit/re-entry chamber. (Wright and Logan)

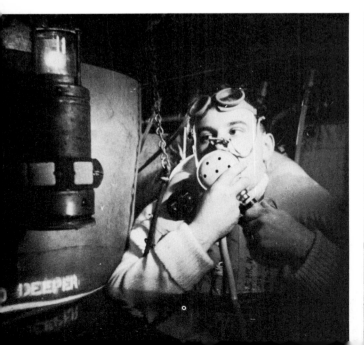

3. The conning tower fitted for escape.

4. Indicator buoys, underwater telephones and signal ejectors.[15]

Developments continued in escape techniques from greater depths, notably the technique of 'hooded ascent' whereby the escaper would breathe the air trapped in the hood of his immersion suit as he went up – the hood providing a built-in reservoir of air. After trials at HMS *Dolphin* the method was tried at sea from HMS *Tiptoe* off Malta in October 1962.[16] Twenty-five pairs of men made successful escapes from depths down to 270 feet using either the free ascent or 'hooded ascent'. For the trials *Tiptoe*'s conning tower was fitted with HIS (Hood Inflation System) in her conning tower which was used to charge the escaper's suit with air. As the escaper rose to the surface air in the suit vented through an exhaust valve into the hood thus ensuring that the air was constantly renewed during the ascent.

By the early 1960s developments in escape technology had come full circle for the T class. The new patrol submarines of the *Porpoise* and *Oberon* classes were fitted with OMECs which did not differ radically from the escape chambers fitted in *Thetis*. But one more T-class submarine was to have her name linked with disaster.

In 1965 HMS *Totem* and HMS *Turpin* were sold to Israel and renamed *Dakar* and *Leviathan* respectively, both boats being extensively refitted by Vickers. Among the modifications carried out, the fin was rebuilt to include a five-man escape chamber: not so much for the purposes of escape but for the covert exit/re-entry of special forces personnel. The Ministry of Defence had wanted *Dakar* to have a proper work-up before proceeding to Israel, but the Israelis were adamant that the boat was required in the Middle East. In January 1968 *Dakar* set out, against the advice of Flag Officer Submarines and MoD, for Israel. The passage to Gibraltar was made on the surface, but *Dakar* was to proceed to Haifa submerged, snorting at night and diving deep during the day. According to instructions *Dakar* was to report her position to Haifa every eight hours. Her estimated date of arrival at Haifa was 2 February 1968, but her commanding officer reported that he would make Haifa on 29 January.

Two minutes after midnight on 25 January 1968, *Dakar* transmitted her routine report, giving her position as 360 miles west of Haifa. Eight hours later, when no report was received, concern began to rise and the duty officer began to call *Dakar* on both naval and international frequencies. When sixteen hours had passed without a signal from *Dakar*, the Israelis declared an emergency. Operational headquarters were set up at RAF Akrotiri in Cyprus, and British, American, Greek, Turkish and Lebanese ships and aircraft joined the search. On 27 January a monitoring station near Nicosia in Cyprus reported an SOS message from a submarine buoy and pin-pointed the position as southeast of Cyprus. Search operations concentrated in this area and a large slick was sighted, but was later found to have come from a Greek tanker. On 31 January the search was finally called off and *Dakar* was declared missing with no hope that her crew could be alive. A year later one of *Dakar*'s indicator buoys was washed up on the Gaza Strip. Her loss has not been attributed to any specific cause, although there are a legion of possibilities: battery explosion, flooding or collision. The possibility that *Dakar* was sunk by the Egyptians was investigated after the Israeli-Egyptian peace agreement, and discounted. The conclusion must be that she was the victim of some catastrophic accident.[17]

An apocryphal legend holds that should a totem-pole presented to HMS *Totem* by a North-American Indian tribe be removed from the submarine, she would be lost. When *Totem* was sold to Israel, the totem-pole was removed and is now in the Submarine Museum. The reader must judge for himself.

9. Toward the Killer Submarine

At the conclusion of hostilities with Japan, the Royal Navy had thirty-two T-class submarines working-up, in service, refitting or going into reserve, and distributed as follows:

Third Submarine Flotilla Home Waters; training and working up: *Talent, Tally-Ho, Tantalus, Templar, Tireless, Truculent, Truncheon*
Fifth Submarine Flotilla Home Waters; training and working-up: *Tactician, Tantivy, Telemachus, Tradewind, Trespasser*
Seventh Submarine Flotilla Home Waters; trials: *Truant*
Second Submarine Flotilla East Indies; operational: *Thrasher, Torbay, Trident*
Fourth Submarine Flotilla Pacific; operational: *Taciturn, Tapir, Taurus, Thorough, Thule, Tiptoe, Totem, Trenchant, Trump, Turpin, Terrapin, Tudor*
Reserve Group D Home Waters: *Tuna*
Awaiting Disposal: *Taku, Tribune, Trusty*[1]

Of the two Dutch Ts, *Zwaardvis* was attached to the Ninth Submarine Flotilla in Home Waters while *Tijgerhaai* was at Aden unattached to a flotilla.

The unpleasant realities of Britain's post-war situation had to be faced, and the transition made from a conscript wartime navy to a volunteer peacetime one. The country was in debt to the USA, Lend-Lease had arbitrarily been suspended and skilled manpower tied-up in the armed services was desperately needed for reconstruction work at home. For the Royal Navy the new mood of 'austerity' meant the cancelling or drastic cutback of new construction, the reassessment of overseas commitments and the disposal of older units of the fleet.

In the general run-down of overseas commitments, the T boats deployed to the British Pacific Fleet were gradually withdrawn. This was partly so that their crews, composed largely of HO (Hostilities Only) ratings could be demobilized, but also on the grounds of expense: although the RN would maintain an East of Suez presence until 1971, the Pacific would become US responsibility. A few submarines were temporarily retained for A/S duties with the surface fleet and in a revival of a pre-war activity anti-piracy patrols off the Chinese coast, but by 1948 all the T boats were in Home Waters or the Mediterranean.

In tandem with the withdrawal of boats from the Far East came the disposal of all the Group One and Two boats still running. These were the old riveted boats: famous names which had borne the brunt of the campaign in the Mediterranean but which were now worn out and which could not be considered for modernization. By the end of 1948 *Tribune, Trident, Taku, Truant, Tuna, Torbay, Thrasher* and *Trusty* together with the war-damaged *Terrapin* were all deleted. Only *Truant* escaped the breaker's torch by running aground in

December 1946 while under tow to Briton Ferry. Their passing was noted with some regret. Captain S.3 wrote in July 1945, when *Tuna* paid off into reserve, that, 'she has given the Hun a good many headaches' and in a reference to her troublesome MAN diesels, 'and the repair staff quite a few'.[2] A further two Ts, *Tapir* and *Taurus*, were lent to the Royal Netherlands Navy in July 1948 to join *Tijgerhaai* and *Zwaardvis*. They were renamed *Zeehond* and *Dolfijn* and were returned to the Royal Navy on 16 July and 8 December 1953 respectively. With the post-war deletions and loans set off against the new construction, the total number of T boats in service by the end of 1948 was 25, distributed as follows:

Second Submarine Flotilla (Portland): *Tireless, Token, Truculent, Truncheon*
Third Submarine Flotilla (Rothesay): *Talent, Tally-Ho, Tantalus, Thermopylae, Tudor, Telemachus* (refit) *Thule* (refit)
Fifth Submarine Flotilla (Portsmouth): *Tactician, Totem, Trump, Turpin*
First Submarine Flotilla (Mediterranean): *Tabard, Tantivy, Templar, Teredo*
Immediate Reserve in the UK: *Taciturn, Tiptoe, Tradewind, Trenchant, Thorough, Trespasser*[3]

The number of Ts available in Home Waters and the Mediterranean was further reduced in 1949 with the

dispatch of three boats to the Far East. No sooner had the last British submarine, HMS *Aeneas*, returned home in December 1948 than FOS/M (Admiral [Submarines] who had adopted the new title of Flag Officer, Submarines, in 1948) was arguing for a number of submarines to be based in Australia for A/S training with the Royal Australian and Royal New Zealand Navies. In September 1949 Admiralty approval was given and the force was to be known as the Fourth Submarine Flotilla.[4] The Flotilla was to consist of three boats based at Sydney of which it was expected that one would be refitting at Singapore. As well as their training role with the RAN and RNZN, the submarines would also provide a limited A/S training capability for the Far East Fleet usually just prior to or after their refits at Singapore. The three boats selected were *Telemachus* and *Thorough* from Home Waters, and *Tactician* from the Mediterranean. *Telemachus* arrived in Sydney on 21 December 1949 followed by *Thorough* on 6 January 1950, joined shortly afterwards by *Tactician*. There was no role, surprisingly in view of their use in special operations in the Second World War, for these submarines during the Korean War, although *Telemachus* was in the war area for A/S training in June 1953.[5]

All the surviving boats were refitted in the immediate post-war period to bring them up to a common stan-

◄
The depot ship *Adamant* at Sydney in late 1945 with a group of seven T boats alongside.

►
The fruits of victory: Stoker Danny Bennett explains the symbols on *Trump*'s 'Jolly Roger' to an appreciative audience when the submarine called at Adelaide during a victory cruise around the coast of Australia. (IWM A.30762)

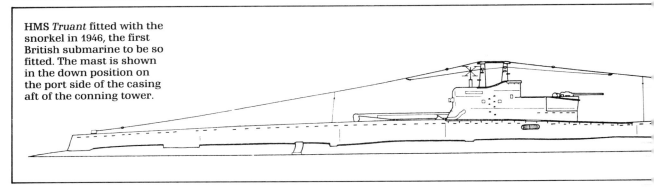

HMS *Truant* fitted with the snorkel in 1946, the first British submarine to be so fitted. The mast is shown in the down position on the port side of the casing aft of the conning tower.

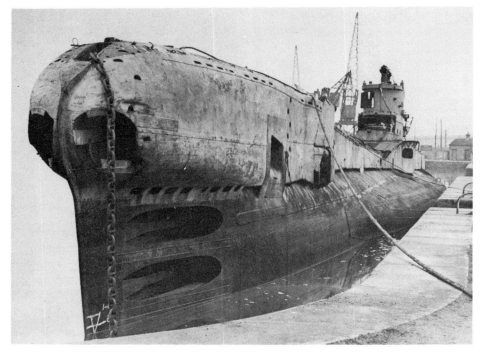

HMS *Thrasher*, known to the Press as the 'Double VC Submarine', returns to Portsmouth in October 1945 to pay off for disposal after service in all three theatres of operations. (Wright and Logan)

HMS *Trident* being broken up at Newport in 1946. *Trident* was one of nine T boats to be scrapped during the immediate post-war period.

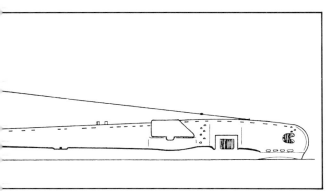

dard. The largest alteration was the fitting of the snorkel, a Dutch device which allowed a submarine to run her diesels while submerged. The Admiralty had shown little interest in the idea pre-war or, indeed, during the war[6] and it was only when the Germans threatened to regain the initiative in the Battle of the Atlantic that serious interest was shown in the device. On 1 November 1944 the Admiralty grudgingly approved the experimental installation of a snorkel, or 'snort' as it became known in British parlance, to one U, S and T class for trials purposes only.[7] *Truant* was selected, since she was the only Vickers-engined T boat in Home Waters available for trials, and was taken in hand at Barrow on 2 March 1945. Vickers completed the work on 5 May 1945.

After work-up and trials, *Truant* (Lieutenant R. S. Brooks) set out to prove the system by undertaking a dived passage to Gibraltar using the snort. She arrived at Gibraltar having remained dived all the time except

for surfacing each day at noon to take sights and report her position. The return journey was less successful: *Truant* remained dived for ten days but was forced to surface when faced with an engine failure.[8]

But, in general, *Truant*'s cruise was a success and the snort was fitted to all the remaining T class: *Tiptoe* being chosen to demonstrate the equipment to HM King George VI at the Clyde Fleet Review in 1947.[9] From 29 April to 26 May 1947 *Taciturn* (Lieutenant-Commander J. M. Mitchell, DSC) carried out a prolonged snort patrol in the Atlantic, snorting by day and diving deep at night, and proving that a 24-hour dived patrol was possible. The longest snort passage undertaken by an unconverted T boat was from 5 to 24 June 1954 when *Tally-Ho* (Lieutenant-Commander B. L. Rowe) made a submerged crossing, apart from surfacing every day at noon to take sights and report her position, of the Atlantic from Bermuda to Portsmouth. The exercise, named 'Snortlant One', was also intended to test the effectiveness of Coastal Command's A/S patrols. All would have gone well had not the asbestos(!) cladding to the exhaust caught fire thus forcing *Tally Ho* to the surface where she was spotted by a Shackleton and subsequently harried for the rest of the journey. The trip did, however, prove that a T boat could undertake a long submerged passage, although Lieutenant-Commander Rowe noted that 'habitability had to be improved'.[10]

The installation was a comparatively simple affair and consisted of a mast containing separate induction/exhaust tubes housed on the casing on the port side of the conning tower. The mast was raised and lowered hydraulically by the telemotor system. At the top of the

▶ A group clustered around the after end of *Truant*'s conning tower in 1945, after the fitting of the first snorkel to a British submarine. The combined induction/exhaust mast can be seen lying in the down position along the casing aft of the conning tower. Note that the Oerlikon gun and platform have been removed and the after end of the conning tower rebuilt. (Ron Slade)

induction tube was a float-controlled head valve to prevent an influx of water should the mast inadvertently dip beneath the sea. When lying flat on the casing the induction tube filled with water which, on raising the mast, drained down into the boat through a hull valve. The drain was also kept open while the boat was 'snorting'. Air was admitted to the engine room down the tube and through a hydraulically operated induction valve in the pressure hull. A telemotor-operated ram opened and shut the valve by means of a fulcrum lever and operating rod sited in the engine room. The induction valve was the most vulnerable part of the system: should the valve fail the boat would flood, and such is believed to have been the cause of the loss of HMS *Affray* in April 1951.[11] After the *Affray* disaster a number of safety features were incorporated into the induction valve to prevent a repetition of the tragedy.

Exhaust from the diesels was discharged through a group exhaust hull valve to a muffler tank in the superstructure and then overboard via the exhaust tube. The exhaust tube filled with water when lowered, but instead of this water being drained into the hull it was blown out by HP air before the engines were started. The exhaust pressure then kept the tube clear. The consequences of sea pressure overcoming the exhaust pressure could be serious, however. In November 1949 *Tudor* (Lieutenant-Commander J. S. Stevens, DSO, DSC) was participating in a major Home Fleet exercise and was snorting while dived in heavy seas. The OOW was trying to maintain periscope depth while keeping beam to sea, the optimum course in such bad weather. The CO noticed a vacuum building up and that the boat was diving: '. . . as I stepped into the control room I heard an expensive noise come from the engine room. One of the diesel main engines had been severely damaged as, before the necessary valves had been shut off, increasing sea pressure overcame the engine exhaust pressure. The engine became filled with sea water and the electric motor to which it was clutched was trying to rotate it.'[12] *Tudor* limped back to Portland on one engine where the damage was made good by HMS *Maidstone*. Some of the engine parts were damaged beyond belief: a connecting rod from one of

▲ As her casing party salutes Flag Officer Submarines' flag at HMS *Dolphin*, *Zeehond* ex-*Tapir* enters Portsmouth harbour during a courtesy call in April 1951. The submarine has been fitted with a snort mast and 267PW radar. (Wright and Logan)

▼ *Taciturn*'s conning tower in 1946, showing the newly installed snort mast in the raised position. The exhaust outlet can be seen facing aft two-thirds of the way up the mast. (IWM FL.4137)

Trespasser's snort mast in the down position lying along the port side of the casing.

the two 1,250bhp Admiralty engines was bent through nearly 180° and was thus exhibited at Fort Blockhouse as proof of the 'incompressibility of water'.[13] A similar accident was to befall *Tireless* in rough weather off Ushant in January 1959.

Fitting the snort meant that the 20mm Oerlikon had to be removed because the bulge of the bandstand would not allow the mast to fit in alongside the conning tower. Added complications arose in the case of the T boats built by the Royal Dockyards where it was found that the addition of the snort had created stability problems. *Truncheon* (Lieutenant-Commander John Coote) was one of the first to report such problems. When surfacing: '. . . *Truncheon* was very bad, she used to lie on her side. It was very wet and potentially dangerous for the people on the bridge. When I complained about this to Flag Officer Submarines' Constructor, he said my complaint was frivolous.'[14] But

the problem would not go away and eventually in March 1949 it was decided to remove the 4-inch gun from these vessels to save topweight.[15] A proposal to remove the two bow externals instead so as to retain the gun was not accepted although eventually all T boats not selected for either Conversion or Streamlining lost their bow externals so that they could carry both the snort and the gun.

At the time the snort seemed the answer to a submariner's prayer: no submarine need risk detection by having to surface at night to charge her batteries and the ability to use her diesels while dived gave a greatly enhanced underwater speed of about 7/8 knots. However, 'snorting' could often be uncomfortable. Should the head of the induction mast dip below the water, either because of heavy sea or if the boat lost trim, the head valve would close. Since the diesels were still running, they were taking their air from inside the boat and causing a vacuum to build up and mens' ears to 'pop'. When the valve was cleared the sudden equalization of pressure was a painful experience.

A more serious problem with snorting concerned battery ventilation. T boats were fitted with two 10-inch × 3-inch fans per battery, able to pass a minimum of 1,000 cubic feet of gas per minute. This was found to be quite adequate for both normal ventilation, when the six fans would be run in series to save power, and charging, when they would be run in parallel. However, when snorting, and the only source of fresh air a 14-inch diameter pipe, the build-up of battery gas and the possibility of an explosion was a real danger.

On 13 June 1950 *Trenchant* (Lieutenant-Commander J. Whitton) was participating in the 1950 annual exercise known as the 'Summer War' which took place to the NW of Ireland. *Trenchant* had been dived for about 9/10 days and had been charging the battery by snorting at night. There had been a high charge/discharge cycle since *Trenchant* had been busy attacking Home Fleet units and demands on the battery had been heavy. Ron Slade was the Radio Electrician and had come off watch at 0400 on 13 June and before turning-in in the forward lower bunk of the POs Mess remarked on the strong smell of battery gas:

'I next awoke and found myself in darkness with occasional flashes of light and little fires obviously started by metal objects falling on the terminals on top of the battery, the heavy battery boards having been blown off by the force of the explosion. In panic I tried to get out, but found my way barred with debris. After frantically shouting for assistance, I saw a light approaching and heard a voice shouting "Is anyone still there?"'

'When I was able to think more clearly I remember that I was sitting under the mess table on the deck with my feet in the battery tank resting on top of the battery. My socks must have been soaked in acid because the bottoms simply rotted away.'[16]

Slade was dragged out by Lieutenant-Commander Whitton and when he reached the control room he found the rest of the crew gathered there or on the bridge, *Trenchant* having surfaced. To extinguish the fires, the area forward of the control room to the torpedo stowage compartment was sealed off and not reopened until there was no further risk. The damage to *Trenchant* was severe: the accommodation area between the control room and the torpedo stowage compartment was completely gutted; four members of the crew were injured, including Slade who sustained bad burns to his legs.

A Board of Inquiry found that due to a fault in the ventilation system there had been an abnormal build-up of battery gas which was probably ignited by a spark from the commutator of one of the battery fans. The explosion lifted the battery boards in the accommodation space, and metal objects, table legs, mess traps, etc., fell on to the cell terminals causing a short circuit. This caused further small fires and explosions. A

Vickers gas-operated machine-gun fell into the battery and was twisted out of all recognition by the 2,000amp current which passed through it!

Trenchant's experience confirmed doubts which had been circulating for some time about safe charging limits for batteries in T boats while snorting. Trials in A-class submarines had shown that hydrogen concentration remained fairly consistent, but for T boats the hydrogen level proved far more variable. Consequently temporary restrictions which had been in force to restrict charging while snorting in T boats were confirmed at the end of June 1950 by the issue of a Submarine General Memorandum.[17] The eventual answer lay in the fitting of hydrogen eliminators: although they could not cure the problem they would prevent the deadly build-up of gas. However, their introduction lay some way in the future.

Experience using the snort on exercises showed that there were numerous tactical disadvantages associated with it. When using the snort, the boat was both blind, since use of the periscopes was wellnigh impossible, and deaf, since the engine noise rendered the ASDIC ineffective. Moreover, the noise of a boat 'snorting' travelled far and wide and the wake of the induction mast formed an easy visual target for aircraft in calm conditions. If a submarine were sighted in such conditions it was not practicable to simply dip the induction mast until the aircraft had passed. Instead, snorting had to be stopped and the mast lowered which affected the trim. Before commencing snorting again, having returned to periscope depth, the complete cycle of raising and draining down the snort mast had to be lowered, which took about 8 minutes. If the induction mast were left up and the boat taken down to 50 feet to cover the snort head, on return to periscope depth it would reappear above the surface and betray the submarine's position to an alert escort of lurking aircraft, before an all-round periscope search could be completed.

Truncheon (Lieutenant John Coote) spent the entire 1948 Summer War dived, but had to resort to withdrawing to a quiet area to use the snort for charging the battery, where she would be out of the way.[18] Snorting was only ever done in daylight when it was good and rough and the tell-tale wake would be hidden. Little or no training was given in the tactical use of the snort, and by September 1950 FOS/M (Rear-Admiral S. M. Raw) was writing that: '. . .one of (his) most important tasks is to teach the submarine commanding officer how and when to snort. Like ammunition it is SAFE only so long as one remembers that it can be VERY dangerous.'[19]

The years 1945 to 1950 were revolutionary for the British submarine service which saw nothing less than a complete reversal of their position within the Royal Navy. Traditionally the submarine service had kept itself at arm's length from the surface fleet, retreated behind the walls of Fort Blockhouse, and fostered a sense of exclusiveness. This attitude fostered a considerable degree of mutual ignorance between the

HMS *Tally-Ho* returns to Fort Blockhouse on 24 June 1954 after her submerged crossing of the Atlantic in Exercise 'Snortland One': this was the longest submerged passage undertaken by an unconverted T-class submarine.

HMS *Trenchant* leaving Portsmouth in April 1949, fitted with a snorkel, but without her 4-inch gun. Dockyard-built T boats fitted with both snort and gun experienced stability problems. (Wright and Logan)

HMS *Truncheon* in April 1951 after her refit by HMS *Montclare*'s staff for the submarine vs. submarine exercises with *Alcide*. Note the removal of the bow externals; the 267PW airguard aerial and the American JT passive hydrophone on the forward casing just aft of the hydroplanes. (Wright and Logan)

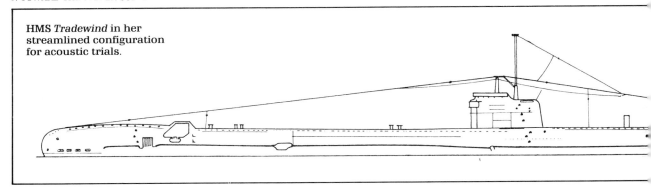

HMS *Tradewind* in her
streamlined configuration
for acoustic trials.

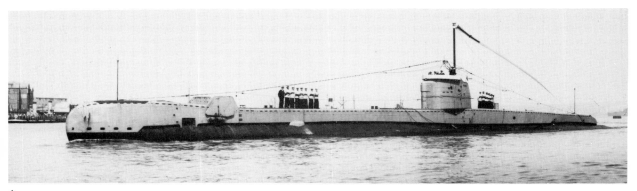

▲
HMS *Tradewind* after
conversion to an acoustic
trials submarine, flying
her paying-off pennant at
Portsmouth in May 1948.
Note the fine line of the
casing with all external

tubes removed and the
much-reduced conning
tower structure. (Wright
and Logan)
▼
HMS *Thule* in April 1957,
restored to front-line

service after completion of
the trials for the 186
'Knout' passive
hydrophone. This
photograph shows the
final development of the
unconverted T-class

'gunboat'. Features to note
are: double 169
transducers; fitting of a
Mk XXIII gun in an
enclosed shield; 267PW
radar and snort mast.
(Wright and Logan)

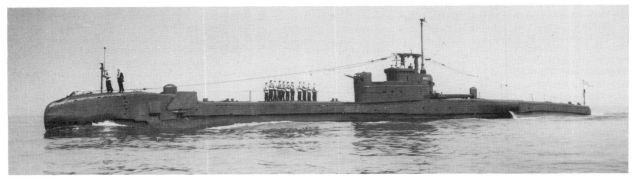

Naval Staff and submariners regarding each other's
priorities. Unlike the Fleet Air Arm, the submarine
branch was not represented on the Admiralty Board.
Its affairs were looked after by a number of Admiralty
departments of which the most important was the
Directorate of Torpedo, Anti-Submarine and Mine Warfare (DTASW) which became the Directorate of Under-
surface Warfare (DUSW) in 1954: a change which
reflected the growing importance of the submarine.
DTASW was often more concerned with the surface
fleet and its attitude to submarines was often hostile.

The end of the war changed all that. The growing
threat posed by the Soviet Navy, and in particular their
submarines built with the aid of liberated German
technology, coupled with the harsh post-war economic
climate which meant that the maintenance of a strong
surface fleet in Home Waters was not possible, brought
the submarine to the forefront of the Staff's attentions.
From the end of 1945 onwards the submarine came to
be viewed as the only means of operating close to the
well-defended Soviet coastline. The Staff accepted that
unrestricted submarine warfare was inevitable and

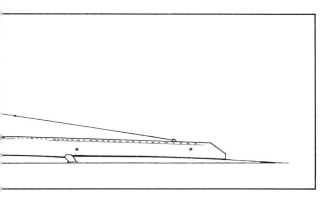

that submarines were '. . . needed to enforce blockade in waters close to the enemy's shores where surface vessels are unable to operate and for special reconnaissance operations.'[20]

The Soviet submarines exiting from their northern bases to prey on British and Allied merchant shipping were seen as the main target and this role was formally recognized in January 1948 when 'the interception and destruction of enemy submarines' was designated the 'primary operational function' of the British submarine fleet. But the ACNS (Rear-Admiral G. A. Oliver) in a paper dated 20 April 1949 went further. He saw the submarine assuming an offensive role off the Soviet coastline, neutralizing the Soviet submarine and surface threat at its source by torpedo attacks and by mining the approaches to the bases. The strength of the submarine arm *vis-à-vis* the drastically curtailed surface fleet was graphically demonstrated a year later when ACNS commented that submarines were one of the few means available to the Royal Navy for 'getting to the enemy on his home ground'.[21]

The new A/S role emphasized the need for a fast yet quiet submarine. The research into noise reduction which had begun during the war was now tackled with increasing vigour. Noise generated by water flowing over the hull, by machinery and by propeller cavitation was a two-edged sword for a submarine because, not only did it 'deafen' the boat's own sensors, but it betrayed her position to a listening enemy. In July 1945 HMS *Tradewind* was taken in hand by Chatham Dockyard for substantial alterations to prepare her for her new role as an acoustic trials vessel. The alterations were quite extensive and comprised: removal of the five external torpedo tubes together with the 4-inch and 20mm gun armament; the blanking off of the orifices for Nos. 1, 2, 5 and 6 tubes (the upper and lower pairs respectively); the bow fined after the removal of 8 and 9 tubes; the bridge and superstructure faired; all gratings on the casing removed and plating fitted in lieu; attack periscope removed and replaced by an ANF radar mast with Type 267 seaguard radar; the Type 129 ASDIC set removed and replaced by a German BALKON passive hydrophone set at the forward end of the ballast keel; a German NIBELUNG ASDIC set fitted forward of the conning tower and lastly a Type 120

retractable ASDIC set fitted. In September 1946 *Tradewind* began a series of trials trundling up and down the improved sound range at Loch Goil. In 1949 she was fitted with a snort, taken from HMS *Taciturn* when the latter was taken in hand for conversion, and began a second series of trials to determine snort-generated noise. Apart from trials there was little use for *Tradewind* in the general submarine fleet and in 1953 she paid off into reserve at Portsmouth and was broken up in July 1955.[22]

But despite the emphasis placed by the Naval Staff on using submarines as ASW platforms, anti-submarine exercises were only item number eleven on FOS/M's list of peacetime activities instructed by the Admiralty.[23] During the Second World War there had been numerous engagements between T boats and U-boats while both were dived, but lack of adequate fire control equipment usually meant both parties warily circling each other. *Talisman*'s attack on *Otus* is believed to have been the first time torpedoes were fired at a submarine while both boats were dived, but the first 'kill' came on 9 February 1945 when *U864* was dispatched by HMS *Venturer* (Lieutenant J. S. Launders) although this successful attack was more the product of what the official history described as 'the most shameful periscope drill'[24] on the part of the U-boat's commander, and Launders' skill and patience than the excellence or sophistication of his equipment.

Exercises were begun at the tactical table at HMS *Osprey* and continued at sea where *Telemachus* (Lieutenant-Commander R. P. Fitzgerald, DSC) and *Tudor* (Lieutenant-Commander J. S. Stevens, DSO, DSC) were some of the first submarines to take part in these manoeuvres. By March 1949 the conclusions had been reached that using present equipment, i.e., the 129/138 combination, a submerged attack on a dived enemy submarine would only be successful if the range were short and the target known to be at periscope depth. The trials also stressed the training of ASDIC operators in both detecting the noise of the enemy boat and the sound of approaching torpedoes. On the subject of weapons FOS/M confirmed that the tried and trusted Mk VIII was quite acceptable for use in submarine vs. submarine attacks, which was just as well for the story of post-war British torpedo development was a dismal one.

In June/July 1950 the first serious submarine vs. submarine exercises were held to simulate the likely effectiveness of a British submarine operating off Soviet bases: the waters around Skye and the smaller islands of Canna, Rumm and Eigg playing the part of the Kola Inlet. The role of the Soviet submarine was 'played' by HMS *Alcide* (Lieutenant M. J. O'Connor): a non-standard A boat fitted with an experimental 152X sonar which was a double transducer variant of the wartime 129 set. The attacking submarine, however, was HMS *Truncheon* (Lieutenant A. Richardson) which had been ingeniously modified by the depot ship HMS *Montclare*'s staff to reduce self-generated noise. Her 4-

inch gun and external bow torpedo tubes were removed to eliminate water flow noise around the hull. *Truncheon* still carried the 129 set in the keel, but was fitted with an American JT precision tracking hydrophone on the forward casing together with a Noise Level Monitor and Cavitation Indicator, which allowed her CO to check the relative amount of noise being made by his submarine.[25]

The quieter hull and superior equipment made *Truncheon* the superior 'hunter killer' and also enhanced her chances of manoeuvring silently into an attacking position. However, the actual results of the trials were not encouraging. Although *Truncheon*'s JT set gave better bearing accuracy and detection ranges, *Truncheon* could only claim eleven successful attacks out of thirty-two sonar-controlled submerged attacks while *Alcide* was able to claim five successes out of seventeen attacks. Neither submarine could manoeuvre silently at more than three knots, and while *Truncheon* was noisily snorting, *Alcide* achieved six 'kills' from seven attacks!

The exercises concluded with a five-day patrol carried out in the Minches south of Skye. *Truncheon* was given a patrol area of forty square miles and was instructed to act as if on an inshore A/S patrol off an enemy defended coast for a continuous period of five days and nights. *Alcide* made eighteen runs through the area during the period: eleven were made while snorting; three on the surface and four dived on motors at 150 feet. *Truncheon* was not forewarned and the number and times of *Alcide*'s sorties were unknown to her. *Truncheon* detected twelve of *Alcide*'s sorties and carried out ten attacks of which four were adjudged successful although no torpedoes were fired and therefore no account taken of any avoiding action by *Alcide*. The six undetected sorties took place during a 48-hour period when adverse weather seriously affected listening conditions.[26]

Although she lost her JT hydrophone to HMS *Dolphin*, *Truncheon* continued the submarine vs. submarine trials where she was pitted against the 'streamlined' *Tireless* and the unconverted *Tally-Ho* in testing approach-and-attack techniques. The result of these trials was that, following the 1951 Summer War both FOS/M and Captain(S) of Third Submarine Flotilla felt confident that British submarines stood a 'fair' chance of destroying enemy submarines in submerged attacks with existing equipment although it was clear that more intensive training would be required. However, it was also noted that: '. . . the present general-purpose submarine, with its gun and other projections, all of which reduce its efficiency as a silent listening platform is, for this reason, unlikely to be very successful in its A/S role.[27]

The end of the decade saw the second batch of deletions: on 26 September 1949 it was announced that *Tantivy*, *Trespasser*, *Tantalus* and *Templar* were to be reduced to category Z reserve prior to breaking up. The tragic loss of *Truculent* following a collision with the Swedish vessel *Divina* on 12 January 1950 ensured *Trespasser*'s retention: she remained in service until July 1961 by which time she was the oldest T boat in the fleet. *Tantalus* was broken up at Milford Haven in November 1950, but a different fate awaited the other two. *Templar* was already in an advanced state of demolition at Lisahally in Northern Ireland when orders were received in 1952 that she was to be converted for use as a dumb target for ASDIC and A/S weapons: she was sunk at Loch Striven in 1950, but raised in December 1958 and subsequently broken up at Troon. *Tantivy* was likewise used as a dumb target, being sunk at Cromarty in 1951 where she remains.

Tudor (Lieutenant W. G. Edwards) took part in Operation 'Musketeer', the Anglo-French operation to regain control of the Suez Canal in November 1956. *Tudor* was tasked for air-sea rescue duties together with the

French submarine *La Créole*. During the operation, *La Créole* gained contact while dived with another potentially hostile submarine (the Egyptian Navy possessed no submarines, but the possible presence of a Soviet boat could not be discounted) which was also dived. *La Créole* began to manoeuvre for a firing position and in accordance with the rules of engagement reported the contact to the Task Force Commander. Fortunately *La Créole* was ordered only to fire in self-defence since the other boat was HMS *Tudor* regaining her position following a navigational error.[28]

For *Tally-Ho, Telemachus, Thule, Tactician, Thorough, Trespasser, Trenchant, Tudor,* the experimental *Trade-wind,* together with the Dutch *Zwaardvis* and *Dolfijn,* the end of the road had been reached in terms of development, although they would continue to serve as both operational and training boats until the early 1960s. But, for *Taciturn, Turpin, Thermopylae, Totem, Truncheon, Tiptoe, Tabard, Trump, Tireless, Teredo, Talent, Token, Tapir* ex-*Zeehond* – following her return by the Dutch – and *Tijgerhaai* a very different future was in store: one that would more than justify Rear-Admiral George Creasy's July 1945 prediction that: 'We stand on the threshold of very considerable technical development and the submarine of the future may differ profoundly from the submersibles of the present and past.'[29]

▲
The Dutch T boats followed a similar line of development: this is *Zwaardvis* in 1954. She has been fitted with a snort mast, but otherwise is little altered. (Royal Netherlands Navy)

◄
Homeward bound: HMS *Telemachus* arriving at Aden in 1959 during her return journey from Australia.

▶
The remains of *Tally-Ho* aground at Briton Ferry in 1967 and already partially demolished. (Dr. Ian Buxton)

10. The Fast Submarine

While the T boats were being adapted for service in the post-war fleet, an entirely separate stream of development was being investigated by the Admiralty, that of the fast submarine. When the Admiralty began to take the threat posed by the German Type XXI U-boat seriously, six S-class submarines were refitted to act as fast underwater targets for ASW training. They lost their gun armament and were streamlined to give minimal resistance: as such they were known as the 'Slippery S'. In her revised configuration *Seraph*'s underwater resistance was reduced by 45 per cent and she achieved a speed of 14.25 knots dived compared to 8.82 knots in an unconverted S boat. At the end of the war a number of German Type XXIs (*U2529*, *U3017*, *U3035*, *U3041* and *U3515*) were used by the Royal Navy for evaluation purposes, and although the submarine was not the 'wonder boat' portrayed in some accounts, it was clear that a lot could be learned. During the post-war period trials were continued with the streamlined HMS *Tradewind* and HMS *Scotsman*, a hybrid S boat fitted with two A-class submarine motors in place of her diesels.

There were four options open to the British in their search for a fast submarine: first to convert one of the Type XXIs to British standards; secondly to pursue the development of Hydrogen Peroxide (HTP) as used in the German Walter type submarines; thirdly to convert an existing T- or A-class submarine, and lastly to design and build an entirely new class of submarine which was, at this stage, known as the Fast Battery Drive boat (FBD).

The conversion of a Type XXI was ruled out on safety and maintenance grounds. Likewise the development of HTP propulsion was very uncertain. It was the third and fourth options that seemed most attractive. On 22 May 1947 FOS/M (Vice-Admiral M. Mansfield) ordered work to start on a preliminary study for converting a T- or A-class submarine. He evidently regarded such a project as no more than a stop-gap for he also ordered detailed design work to begin on the FBD boat: this submarine would eventually emerge as HMS *Porpoise*, but not for some time. Mansfield's enthusiasm for the conversion scheme was evidently stimulated by a paper put forward by A. J. Sims, a Chief Constructor, on 18 May 1947, in which he had advocated limited streamlining of the casing and superstructure and the insertion of an extra battery section under the control room.[1]

Work on the new design proceeded quickly, no doubt aided by the new emphasis placed on the submarine as an offensive weapon. At a Controller's meeting on 22 June 1947 it was reported that the preliminary study showed that conversion of a T boat was more practicable than an A boat since the Ts already had three battery sections and a fourth could be fitted in under the control room, displacing the oil fuel tanks there, multiplying the total power by 2.5 and giving an underwater speed of 14–15 knots. At the same time the casing would be streamlined, but the existing hull form would be retained. Sims argued, however, that a better arrangement would be to insert the extra battery section by cutting the pressure hull at the after end of the control room and inserting a 3–4 frame space. DNC

Lady Tovey, wife of Admiral of the Fleet Lord Tovey, holds *Turpin*'s bell during the recommissioning ceremony at Chatham in September 1951. Lieutenant-Commander John Roxburgh, who had previously commanded *Tapir* during the Second World War, stands on the right. Note the low bridge at the forward end of the fin.

was requested to make a detailed study of the possibilities with the view to beginning work on the first submarine during the next financial year.

DNC produced two schemes for such a conversion. Scheme 'A' was relatively straightforward and followed Sims's original idea of May 1947 as follows:

1. All non-essential external appendages removed, gun armament and superstructure faired.
2. Bridge redesigned to accommodate revised arrangements of periscopes, radio masts, snort induction and exhaust with supports for all these masts.
3. Bow shutters fitted to internal torpedo tubes, resulting in some redesign of the bow.
4. Complete arrangement of the control room to suit modern practice. Bridge to be repositioned ahead of the forward periscope.
5. No. 3 battery beneath the control room to be rearranged and a new battery to be fitted in place of OFTs 84–98: battery ventilation to be modified as necessary.
6. Main flat of the control room to be raised by 2 inches.
7. Top strake of the pressure hull in way of the bridge to be removed and renewed to facilitate points 2, 5 and 6 above.

◀
HMS *Taciturn*, first of the T-Conversions in March 1951 on completion of the refit.

▶
A view of *Totem*'s, somewhat damaged bows in 1953, showing the shutters over the bow tubes and the fine lines to the hull.

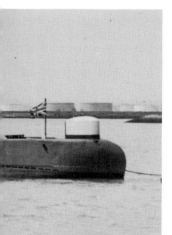

8. Rearrangement of oil fuel in external tanks to obtain a satisfactory trim and accommodate some of the fuel lost as a result of 5.
9. Modifications to forward and after hydroplanes to deal with increased underwater speeds.

Scheme 'B' consisted of points 1 to 9 as above, but with the following additions:

10. An extra pair of T-class motors, one per shaft, in tandem with the existing motors capable of 6,000shp (maximum) and thereby using the maximum output of which batteries are capable for a short time.
11. 14 feet of parallel pressure hull inserted aft of 98 station to accommodate extra motors and larger switchboards. The external hull to be lengthened accordingly and faired into existing lines.
12. Resiting of engines to effect 10.
13. Fitting larger thrust-blocks and an additional clutch between the two motors on each shaft.
14. In both schemes existing shafts and motors would be retained.

A comparison of 'A' and 'B' is as follows:

	Design 'A'	Design 'B'
Length:	276ft	290ft
Beam:	26ft 6in	26ft 6in
Displacement:		
surface	1,453 tons	1,540 tons
dived	1,565 tons	1,675 tons
Max. speed on motors:	14.5 knots	16.75 knots
Max. SHP on motors:	4,000	6,000
Max. RPM on motors:	550	615
Endurance on motors at:		
10 knots:	6 hours	5.25 hours
12 knots:	2.75 hours	2.50 hours
14 knots:	0.6 hours	1.25 hours
15 knots:	0	0.75 hours
Max. snort speed:	10 knots	10 knots
Endurance while snorting		
at 10 knots:	7,300nm	7,300nm+[2]

Design 'B' was the more advantageous design in that the submarine had a far higher underwater speed of 2 knots+ on Design 'A' and the fitting of two additional motors gave flexibility of drive: two motors could be used for drive while the other pair could be charging the battery – a preferable arrangement to running on one motor while charging with the other. Other advantages included a more spacious control room and enhanced diesel endurance since the magazine could be converted to an OFT. In Design 'A' the magazine would be required to hold additional control room equipment.

The Ship Design Committee, which met on 2° April 1948, were evidently of the same mind for they opted for 'B' and approved two T class being taken in hand for conversion, despite the fact that 'B' cost £410,000 against £330,000 for 'A' and that there was no special provision in the Naval Estimates for this work. The formal Staff Requirement was issued on 20 May 1948 which laid down the operational function of the new 'Conversions' and is fully quoted in Appendix 4, but briefly demanded that the T Conversion or 'Super T', as they were soon known, be capable of performing 'the

functions of a fully operational submarine capable of carrying out a war patrol continuously submerged' combined with the 'highest possible submerged speed'.[3] The approval of the Admiralty Board was obtained on 21 March 1949 for the final design:

Length:	
pressure hull:	258ft
waterline:	271ft 3in
overall:	285ft 4in
Beam (extreme):	26ft 6½in
Surface Draught:	
forward in diving trim:	15ft 1½in
aft in diving trim:	16ft 4in
Corresponding displacement:	
surface:	1,565 tons
standard:	1,260 tons
dived:	1,680 tons
SHP of engines:	2,500
Speed at surface displacement:	15 knots
Oil fuel on legend displacement:	210 tons
Endurance at 12 knots:	11,500nm
Battery:	
no. of cells:	448
no. of motors:	4
HP of main motors:	6,000
Dived speed for 20 minutes:	17 knots
Dived Endurance:	
at 14½ knots:	1 hour
at 8 knots:	11 hours
Armament:	
torpedo tubes:	Six 21-inch forward
reloads:	Six
guns:	None
mines:	As requisite
Complement:	60
Diving Depth:	350 feet

By the time Board approval had been given, the first two boats had been selected for conversion (dates of their conversions are given in parentheses): *Taciturn* (November 1948–March 1951) and *Turpin* (June 1949–September 1951). The next pair were *Thermopylae*

HMS *Tiptoe*, one of the last four Conversions to be lengthened by 17 feet 6 inches. In this photograph she is shown with both radar W/T masts raised.

The Dutch *Tijgerhaai* in her partially streamlined configuration in 1962. Note the absence of external torpedo tubes and the fairing around the periscope standards. (Wright and Logan)

(September 1951–1952) and *Totem* (1951–May 1953) followed by *Tiptoe* (July 1952–September 1954) and *Truncheon* (September 1951–December 1953), the latter being due for refit after her pioneering trials, which brought the total to six. The general rearmament which followed the Korean War put another two boats back into the programme and *Tabard* (March 1953–May 1955) and *Trump* (February 1954–June 1956) were the last two selected. All the boats selected were of welded construction and the work was to be carried out by the Royal Dockyard at Chatham.

When *Taciturn* commissioned on 12 March 1951 she looked totally different. The characteristic T-boat casing with its various lumps and bumps, containing the external torpedo tubes, had gone, to be replaced by a smooth, even casing running the full length of the hull. The conning tower had been replaced by a large fin containing the seven various periscopes and masts which from forward to aft were: 9½-inch attack periscope, 9½-inch search periscope, 267PW airguard aerial, 267PW seaguard aerial, telescopic snort induction mast fitted with a ball float valve at the upper end, periscopic wireless mast carrying VHF and HF aerials with X-Band radar intercept equipment and telescopic

snort exhaust mast. *Taciturn* was the first British submarine to have separate induction and exhaust masts, and after the *Affray* disaster was the only submarine permitted to use her snorkel. The bridge was a small cockpit-like structure fitted forward of the fin and entered via the old gun tower. The new bridge was at a lower level than that in an unconverted T boat and would prove to be the source of problems later on.

The 14-feet extension of the pressure hull was inserted aft of the engine room bulkhead. Lengthening the hull meant that there had to be some rearrangement of the tanks. Internally No. 4 fresh water tank was converted to a compensating tank and an additional distilled water tank fitted serving 3 and 4 battery compartments. No. 2 ballast tanks were converted to fuel tanks and the No. 3 ballast tanks which had been converted to oil fuel stowage reverted to their original role as ballast tanks. Their capacity was increased by roughly 20 tons by extending them aft over 'O' compensating and 'Q' tanks taking in part of No. 4 ballast tanks, the remaining portion of No. 4 being converted to permanent oil fuel stowage. No. 5 emergency fuel tanks were to be made permanent and their Kingstons removed. Additional fuel tanks were to be inserted in way of the additional section of the pressure hull and No. 6 ballast tanks were to be reduced in size by moving their forward bulkhead aft.

These modifications gave a single ballast tank forward (No. 1), which was to be supplemented by a buoyancy tank, a pair of tanks amidships (No. 2) and a pair aft (No. 3). Between 2 and 3 ballast tanks there were two groups of four fuel tanks.[4]

Internally the biggest change was in the rearranged machinery spaces with the additional pair of motors and the new control room with its separate W/T, radar and ASDIC offices – the latter known as the Sound Room and built at the starboard forward corner of the control room and designed to withstand an external and internal pressure of 1psi with the door and all other openings blanked up in order to limit fluctuations in pressure when the boat was snorting.

Taciturn ran her first of class trials in October/November 1951. Surface speed with direct drive was 13.2 knots at 433rpm – little better than before conversion – but when using diesel electric drive she made 17 knots at 620rpm, a significant improvement. Maximum submerged speed was 15.4 knots at 90 feet at 615rpm. However, it was found that the high rpm could not be maintained so a top speed of 15 knots at 590rpm was settled on. Snorting speed was 9.25 knots at 400rpm and *Taciturn* had a dived endurance of 32 hours at 3.2 knots. Further trials found that opening the bow torpedo shutter when dived at 90 feet caused the loss of 1 knot

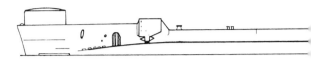

HMS *Thermopylae*: one of the three T Conversions lengthened by 14 feet. Note the low bridge at the forward end of the fin enclosing the masts and the dome at the bow for the ill-fated 171 'Four Square' sonar set.

when running at full speed, but that turning in the fore planes gave an increase of one knot when running dived at 90 feet at full speed.[5]

However, it is clear that many of the T Conversions routinely exceeded 15 knots while dived. *Totem* (Commander John Coote) recorded regularly going at 18 knots during A/S exercises in the Mediterranean: 'It was like money for old rope, we'd just pop under the layer, wind on 18 knots and we would clear a mile in four minutes. Follow that with ten minutes silent running under the layer at 12 knots and we would be 3 miles from the escort.'[6] However, one contributory factor as to why *Totem* was, in her day, one of the faster T Conversions was the unauthorized removal of

◀
HMS *Truncheon* at Helsinki in the early 1960s, showing her snort induction mast raised.

▶
HMS *Tireless*, first of the T-Streamlines, at speed off the Devon coast during trials in August 1952.

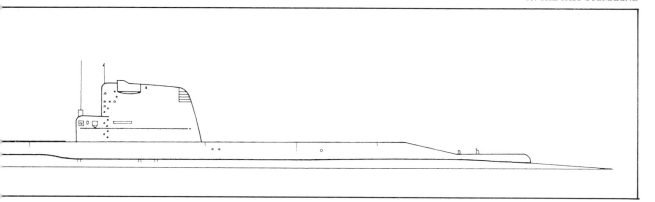

the 'bird-bath' housing the airguard aerial at the top of her fin. The work was done by the depot ship at Malta where the authorities proved more amenable to such modifications! Without the 'bird-bath' *Totem* could add another ¾-knot to her dived speed.

Taciturn was followed by *Turpin*, *Totem* and *Thermopylae*. *Turpin* was lengthened by only 12 feet, but *Totem* and *Thermopylae* were lengthened by 14 feet. The conversion programme had not gone unnoticed by the Dutch who in October 1951 inquired about the practicability of converting *Tijgerhaai* and *Zwaardvis*. They .were informed that there was no reason why *Tijgerhaai* should not be converted, but *Zwaardvis* was not suited owing to her partially riveted hull. *Tijgerhaai* received a

partial streamlining. Her casing was fined, the external torpedo tubes were removed and she was given a fairing around her periscope standards presumably to improve the water flow, and thereby reduce noise, when dived.

Taciturn and *Turpin* had been running for barely 6 months before serious concern was expressed about their stability. In October 1951 an investigation of the seaworthiness of the first two T Conversions was carried out by the Assistant Director of Naval Construction, G. Bryant, and showed that in the deep surface condition *Taciturn* had a metacentric height of 8.8 inches and 8.5 inches for *Turpin*. At the time, the next pair, *Thermopylae* and *Totem*, were under construction

and preparations were in hand for the fifth and sixth boats, *Truncheon* and *Tiptoe*, to be taken in hand. An inclining experiment with *Truncheon* before conversion showed that her GM would be about 2 inches worse than *Turpin*. This was considered unacceptable: '*anything* worse than *Turpin* would be unacceptable'.[7] Bryant went on to note that, 'although the safety of the ship at large angles [of heel] is not in doubt, there may be complaints of heavy rolling on the surface'.[8]

Bryant was quite correct. Reports began to come in from sea about their performance; heavy rolling on the surface was a frequent complaint. *Turpin*'s CO, Lieutenant-Commander J. C. Y. Roxburgh, complained that after a surface passage across the North Sea in company with *Maidstone* and other, unconverted, submarines he was told by other COs that they could keep their charts on the bridge while *Turpin* endured a 'wet and unpleasant' crossing.[9]

The low bridge, 'that abortion of a low bridge',[10] was a particular focus for complaints: '. . . when we had to be on the surface in bad weather it was untenable . . . in fact we shut the upper lid and ran on the induction mast and kept watch using the search periscope'.[11] The problem lay in that the height of the bridge had been reduced by 2 feet 6 inches compared with an unconverted T boat, which when combined with the reduction in draught due to carrying oil fuel in external tanks gave a 3 foot 6 inch reduction in freeboard. This was accepted in the interests of improved underwater performance and reduction of topweight. The consequences for those at sea in a T Conversion were

unpleasant: in December 1952 *Thermopylae*'s OOW was knocked unconscious when a wave swept over the bridge, and in the same month *Taciturn* (Lieutenant-Commander J. M. Mitchell, DSC) had a very rough time during Exercise 'Mainbrace'. Her CO reported that on six out of sixteen nights it was impossible to maintain an adequate bridge lookout. Off Jan Mayen Island, riding a sea at 11 knots with a swell 15 feet high and 200 feet long, the submarine began to poop: '. . . the stern failed to rise to the sea: the ship hung in the trough and a wave swept over her from aft completely engulfing the bridge. The force of such a sea is terrible to feel . . . once begun it could not be stopped. Speed was reduced to 7 knots and then to 5 knots. Course was altered to put the sea astern and on either quarter. As a last resort speed was increased to 12 knots, the after planes put to 15° and the ship steamed stern to sea. Still every five minutes the sea flooded over and to avoid injury the ship was hove head-to-sea . . . deciding we had come to the limits of our endurance I shut down the bridge and stationed the OOW in the control room.'[12]

The solution was twofold. In the boats already converted No. 3 main ballast tank was combined with No. 2 emergency oil fuel tank to form a combined ballast/EOF tank. This would increase reserve of buoyancy, freeboard and stability in the full buoyancy condition. Approval to make the necessary alterations was given on 2 February 1953 and was first carried out in *Totem*. However, as a result of the alterations, diving time would be cut since No. 3 main ballast tank had

◀ HMS *Tabard* on 27 June 1955, showing the larger fin which incorporated the bridge position. Note that the submarine is fitted with a single 168 transducer in the bow.

▶ HMS *Token* on 6 January 1956, following her streamlining. Note the frame for the HF transmitting aerial, the dome for the 168 transducers on the after casing (the second is barely visible forward) and the platform forward of the conning tower for the Mk XXIII gun. (IWM FL.3772)

◀ HMS *Tireless* at sea in August 1959, showing her more primitive snort arrangements: the mast is in the raised position aft of the conning tower.

increased by some 50 tons without any increase in the flooding or venting arrangements. It was also considered that to avoid restrictions in the ranges of water density in which the boat could dive with no emergency oil fuel on board, the amount of fresh water would have to be cut by four tons to 25 tons and the amount of lubricating oil from sixteen to eleven tons. The effect of the combining of the tanks can be roughly summarized as:

	Original T Class	T Conversion Existing	T Conversion Modified
Reserve of buoyancy:	260 tons	150 tons	200 tons
Freeboard from top of CT:	13ft	9ft 6in	10ft
Surface GM:	14½in	10in (approx.)	13in (approx.)

For the four remaining boats the solution was more radical. Instead of a 14-foot extension to the hull, a 17-foot 6-inch extension was added – the extra 3 feet 6 inches going in the control room to ease congestion there. The forward and after ends of the casing were to be constructed of aluminium alloy to save weight. DNC emphasized that the extra space was not to be used to carry additional equipment otherwise the purpose of the alteration – to increase buoyancy – would not be achieved. He also impressed the need to save weight at all times during the conversion. A further modification was to build the fin from aluminium panels supported on a steel lattice framework and incorporate the bridge into the fin structure

proper. However, only *Tabard* and *Trump* appeared in this form.

Conversion of a T-class submarine was a complicated operation, yet the *Truncheon/Alcide* exercises had shown what could be achieved by a limited streamlining. Accordingly in December 1950 FOS/M received approval to commence work on streamlining older – riveted – boats early in 1951.[13] The first boat – HMS *Tireless* – was taken in hand at the end of 1951. The remaining boats were *Tapir* (on her return by the Dutch), *Talent*, *Teredo* and *Token*. The work carried out was relatively simple and was carried out during normal refit periods. The gun and external torpedo tubes were removed, but No. 11 tube was retained to give a stern shot lacking in the conversions. The casing was rebuilt and faired, the bridge rebuilt and raised to enclose the masts and periscope standards. Snort arrangements were not altered: a combined induction/ exhaust mast was fitted on the port side aft of the conning tower. A high-capacity battery was installed giving a 23 per cent increase in power. Internally the boats were little altered apart from the installation of a sound room in the control room.

On completion of the refit *Tireless* underwent the usual 'first of class' trials which included a comparative trial with an unconverted snort-fitted T boat, HMS *Tudor*. Seven trials were carried out to determine differences in under-water endurance, surface turning, submerged turning, acceleration and deceleration, diving trials, depth-changing and submerged speed.[14] The trials, carried out in October 1952, showed that the streamlining of the hull and the high-capacity battery gave *Tireless* an increase of 30–40 miles in underwater endurance throughout the speed range compared with *Tudor*. There was little difference in surface performance since the underwater hull had not been altered, but it was noticed that the increase in the height of the bridge was a considerable improvement to surface watchkeeping in moderate or rough weather.

In submerged turning trials *Tireless* turned at about 10° smaller than *Tudor* at most speeds with 35° rudder, but with only 20° rudder the position was reversed. The discrepancy was 'unexplained'[15] since it was anticipated that *Tireless*'s large fin would reduce her turning circle. There was little change in relative acceleration/deceleration rates between the two boats, the small differences being ascribed to the reactions of individual crew members in carrying out orders. There was no appreciable difference in diving time, but in changing depth *Tireless* reached the required depth and returned to periscope depth faster than *Tudor*, almost certainly due to her higher speed. The greatest difference between the two was in underwater speed as shown in the table below:

	Tireless	Tudor
Revs per knot:	40	48
Max. speed at periscope depth at 380rpm:	9.5 knots	8.1 knots
Max. quiet speed before cavitation occurs:	3.25 knots	2.3 knots
Max. RPM before cavitation occurs:	125	110[16]

Thus the principal effects of the streamlining were twofold. First the speed per RPM was greater and secondly the RPM at which cavitation occurred was also greater. Thus not only could *Tireless* go faster than *Tudor*: she could go faster while making less noise – an important factor when 'acoustic housekeeping' was beginning to make its presence felt in the submarine fleet. *Token* was the only other Streamline refitted at Devonport Dockyard, *Tapir*, *Teredo* and *Talent* being refitted at Chatham. *Tapir*'s refit was delayed by suspicion of sabotage in 1954,[17] but *Talent* suffered a far more serious accident. The submarine was in No. 3 dock at Chatham in December 1954 and the work was well in hand: the old casing and conning tower being already partially demolished. On the afternoon of 15 December there was an abnormally high tide and seconds after 15.30 the caisson at the entrance to the dock was observed to lift and having risen about 6 inches water began to flood into the dock: '. . . securing chains then broke and the caisson impaled itself at a slight angle on *Talent*'s stern. The caisson was then swept up the dock on the port side of the S/M coming to rest at the NE end of the dock. The S/M was then swept off its blocks and was carried out of the dock on the backwash stern first at high speed into the river where she grounded on the far bank.'[18] Three dockyard workmen lost their lives in the accident. *Talent* was pumped out, secured alongside the salvage vessel *Swin*

and returned to the yard. The Admiralty's first suspicion was that further sabotage might have been responsible, but on investigation it was discovered that the caisson had been insufficiently ballasted. This was, however, the only accident in a very successful programme, which reflected very highly on the submarine staff at Chatham Dockyard who bore the brunt of the work. *Talent*, however, was to be singularly unfortunate: in 1956 she was rammed by a merchant ship while dived off St. Catherine's Head, Isle of Wight, and sustained severe damage to her conning tower.

The Conversions and Streamlines served mainly in Home Waters with the 2nd, 3rd and 5th Squadrons (Flotillas had become Squadrons in 1952 with the adoption of US-style nomenclature) and in the Mediterranean with the 1st Submarine Squadron, the latter changing its title to 5th Submarine Squadron when the 1st Submarine Squadron returned to Fort Blockhouse. The 4th Submarine Squadron remained in Australia.

Those serving in Home Waters or the Mediterranean, however, did deploy farther afield. In 1954 *Taciturn* (Lieutenant-Commander P. Murray-Jones) made a submerged passage using her snort from Bermuda to her

HMS *Tireless*; first of the five T Streamlines. In this drawing she is shown with the dome for a 168 sonar set forward, with her 276PW seaguard radar aerial raised and with the snorkel in the down position. The bracket on the after casing is for supporting the HF transmitting aerial.

◀▲
More misfortune: the port side of *Talent's* damaged conning tower after being rammed by a merchant ship while dived off St. Catherine's Head in 1956. (Royal Navy Submarine Museum)

▲
Talent's hull aground and secured to the salvage vessel *Swin* after being swept out of No. 3 Dock at Chatham on 15 December 1954. (Royal Navy Submarine Museum)

▶
HMS *Talent* 'blowing out' before diving during exercises with HMS *Hermes* in June 1966.

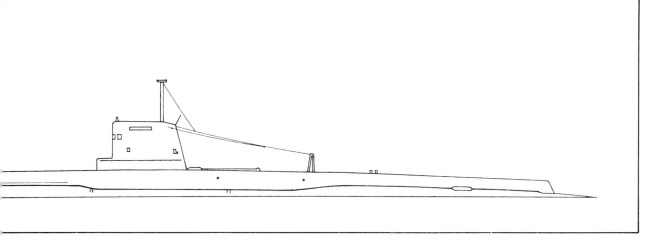

patrol position north of the Shetlands during Exercise 'Bright Bonfire Nine', remaining submerged from 11 October to 12 November[19] – the longest dived passage carried out by any T-class submarine. In 1958 *Turpin* (Lieutenant-Commander A. D. Roake) deployed to the Caribbean, but had to be towed home after cracks were discovered in the main engine frames which would not allow her to return to the UK under her own power. In a situation reminiscent of HMS *Tribune*'s journey across the Atlantic in 1941, the port engine was shored up with girders by men of the Royal Electrical and Mechanical Engineers (REME) detachment in Jamaica, while the starboard engine was strapped up to enable it to be used to provide a charge during the homeward tow. *Turpin* left Kingston, Jamaica, on 11 March in tow of the tug *Samsonia* and arrived at Devonport on 9 April 1958. On the morning of departure Lieutenant-Commander Roake noticed ten carrion crows surrounding the house in which he was staying: hardly a good omen! Fortunately the 5,200-mile tow passed off without incident, taking 28 days at an average speed of 7½ knots.[20]

In 1960, *Tabard*, *Trump* and *Taciturn* went farther afield, going to Australia to join the 4th Submarine Squadron and relieve *Tactician*, *Telemachus* and *Thorough*. *Tabard* was the first to arrive in November 1960 followed by *Trump* in June 1961 and *Taciturn* in 1962.

Their role remained the same: to provide ASW training for the Royal Australian and Royal New Zealand Navies together with units of Britain's Far Eastern Fleet as well as units of various SEATO navies.

While in the Far East, *Trump* (Lieutenant-Commander J. B. L. Watson) suffered a serious accident when a seaman, LME M. Hillman, was badly injured during a maintenance period alongside at Sydney. Work was being carried out on the telemotor lines operating the bow caps for the port bank of torpedo tubes. At the same time the torpedo in No. 4 tube was partially withdrawn for routine maintenance. While work on the torpedo was in progress, PO Alan Scrivenor, *Trump*'s TI, heard water entering the compartment. On checking he found that the bow-cap indicator for No. 4 tube showed that the cap was slightly open. He immediately worked the hand emergency pump, but found that the flow of water increased and realized that the pressure on the telemotor system to the bow caps had been reversed so that his attempt to shut the bow cap had achieved the opposite. To shut the bow cap Scrivenor would have to move the operating lever to 'Open' but this was impossible since safety interlocks prevented the bow cap being opened while the rear door was open. To shut the bow cap, the interlock had to be removed, so working on his knees, without proper tools and with the water level steadily rising, Scrivenor

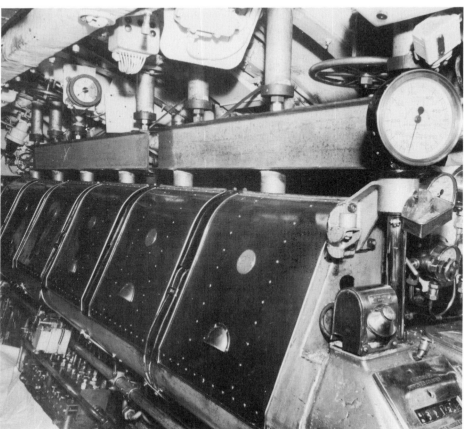

▶ HMS *Trump* passing under Sydney's harbour bridge in November 1968. Note the large dome for the 187 sonar in the bow. (Royal Navy Submarine Museum)

◀ HMS *Turpin*'s port engine showing the shoring installed by the ship's company with REME assistance after cracks developed in the main engine frames. (Royal Navy Submarine Museum)

▶ HMS *Tabard* coming alongside at Fort Blockhouse in July 1968 on her return from the Far East with the traditional paying-off pennant flying from the W/T mast. (Royal Navy Submarine Museum)

set about his task. Meanwhile the OOD, Lieutenant A. P. Hoddinott, arrived and organized a party to haul the torpedo back into the tube using block and tackle. The tail of the torpedo had just passed over the sill of the door frame when the tackle parted and the torpedo trundled back out for about half its length, trapping LME Hillman against the coaming leading aft into the fore ends. The situation was finally resolved when Scrivenor removed the interlock and was able to close the bow cap. The torpedo was duly hauled back and the compartment pumped out. A subsequent inquiry commended PO Scrivenor for his actions and found that no single person was to blame, but that greater co-ordination between departments was required when organizing repair and maintenance work.[21]

The three boats remained in the Far East until the late 1960s when cuts in British defence spending and the Australian acquisition of six Oberon-class submarines rendered their presence unnecessary. Taciturn was the first to return home in 1966 followed by Tabard in March 1968 and Trump in January 1969. Tabard came home across the Pacific, making a 14,406 nautical mile semi-circumnavigation of the world via the Panama Canal.

Until the appearance of the first of the Fast Battery Drive boats, HMS Porpoise, in 1958, the eight T Conversions were the most advanced conventional submarines in service with the Royal Navy. They took part in every major exercise and proved highly effective. Although smaller they were roughly comparable in performance to the American GUPPY (Greater Underwater Propulsive Power) conversions, although their diving depth was slightly less: 300 feet as opposed to 400 feet.[22] Apart from the short-lived R-class submarines built at the end of the First World War, the T Conversions were the Royal Navy's first operational fast submarines and the experience gained in them was invaluable in operating the Porpoise/Oberon boats as well as the nuclear-powered hunter killers, the first of which, HMS Dreadnought, commissioned in 1963.

But in the early 1960s their age began to tell against them. The last of the unconverted 'gunboats' in the Royal Navy, HMS Tudor, was sold in July 1963 and arrived at Faslane in the same month for breaking up.

The other surviving 'gunboat', the Dutch *Zwaardvis*, went at about the same time: *Zwaardvis* was sold to breakers at Antwerp on 12 July 1963 followed quickly by *Tijgerhaai* which was sold to breakers at Amsterdam on 5 November 1965. Three of the class were sold to Israel, the deal being announced in November 1964 after protracted negotiations. The boats were handed over in 1965–6: *Turpin* became *Leviathan*, *Totem* became *Dakar* and *Truncheon* became *Dolphin*. All three were extensively refitted by Vickers before being commissioned by their new owners: *Leviathan* on 19 May 1967; *Dakar* on 10 November 1967 and *Dolphin* on 9 January 1968.

Leviathan arrived in Israeli waters in June 1967. *Dakar* was due to arrive in January 1968, but was lost on passage; *Dolphin* arrived in February 1968. *Leviathan* paid off for disposal in 1974, but *Dolphin* was operational at the time of the Yom Kippur War (1973–4). Her operations are shrouded in secrecy, but it is almost certain that she took part in special operations against Egyptian harbour installations. She eventually paid off in 1977; the last operational T boat.

For the boats in the Royal Navy, the 1960s represented a steady parade to the block as they were gradually paid off, placed on the disposal list and then sold to the breakers. *Teredo* was the first of the converted boats to go, being sold in June 1965 for subsequent breaking up at Faslane, and was followed in chronological order by *Tapir* (December 1966), *Tireless* (September 1968), *Talent* (1969), *Token* (February 1970), *Thermopylae* (May 1970), *Tiptoe* (April 1971), *Trump* (July 1971), *Taciturn* (July 1971) and *Tabard* (January 1974). The latter had, in fact, paid off on 14 June 1968 on her return from Australia, but enjoyed an extended lease of life as harbour training vessel at Fort Blockhouse before following her sisters to the breakers.[23] The last operational British T boat was *Tiptoe* which, under the command of Lieutenant-Commander J. J. Daniel, finally paid off on 29 August 1969 after 25 years in commission.

In Harry Pounds' scrapyard at the northern end of Portsmouth Harbour, lies the rusting after end of a submarine; the remains of HMS *Tiptoe* and all that is left of fifty-three T-class submarines.

◄
The handing over of HMS *Totem* to Israel at Portsmouth on 28 June 1965. Flag Officer Submarines, Vice-Admiral Sir Ian McGeogh, stands on the pontoon while the new Israeli CO goes aboard. Note the Israeli jack flying and her new name, *Dakar*, on the conning tower. (Royal Navy Submarine Museum)

►
Dolphin, ex-*Truncheon*, in the eastern Mediterranean. She was the last operational T boat.

▼
HMS *Token* diving in September 1967.

11. In Retrospect

Were the T class a good design? With so many differing views on what constitutes a 'good design', it is not an easy question to answer. The naval architect will regard the design as successful if his work meets the staff requirements at a reasonable cost. The officers and men who have to live and fight in the ship attach considerable importance to habitability and looks. Lastly the historian, looking back with the benefits of hindsight, will have a different view.

To be seen as a 'good design' a ship will be part of an evolutionary chain rather than an exciting prototype. She must be successful in her primary role while being capable of other tasks. She must be economical, though not necessarily cheap, to build and yet have margins for the addition of new equipment. She must be 'versatile, adaptable and developable'.[1] Lastly, the ship must have an acceptable standard of habitability: a ship that is decidedly uncomfortable to live in can became an operational liability. Each of these individual aspects must be right: weakness in any part degrades the whole.

During the inter-war period the Royal Navy built the large, and unreliable, submarines of the O, P and R classes and in doing so neglected much of the experience acquired during the testing years of the Great War. The T class, however, marked a return to a line of submarine development which had begun with *A.1*, the Royal Navy's first 'in-house' submarine design, and which had ended with the highly successful L class, designed during the First World War.

Operationally, the T class must be considered successful in their primary role: the sinking of enemy ships. Their size enabled them to carry more torpedoes than any other British submarine and they possessed qualities of endurance enabling them to travel considerable distances to their patrol position and remain on patrol longer in all the theatres of war except for the Far East where the pre-war planners had not envisaged the rapid Japanese advance and the resulting loss of the bases at Hong Kong and Singapore. The class were also successful in other roles: special operations, store carrying and minelaying to name but a few.

The T class were the largest submarines to be built by the Royal Navy during the Second World War and thus were not cheap. Yet their size ensured that they could accept numerous modifications and additions without compromising the original design. During the post-war period the T Conversions and Streamlines adopted an entirely new primary role, anti-submarine warfare, with considerable success. Although the cost of a conversion was almost as much as that of a wartime submarine, it was considerably cheaper than building a new boat. In the strained condition of the British economy in the post-war decade, this was an important consideration.

In terms of habitability then, in as much as any submarine could be described as 'comfortable', the T class possessed a good standard of accommodation and were popular with their crews.

The twentieth century has seen a remarkable transition in the role and capabilities of the submarine. In 1938, when HMS *Triton* commissioned, submarines were slow, had to surface to charge their batteries and carried a mixed gun and torpedo armament. The submarines of today, including the new T class, some of which bear the names of their illustrious predecessors, are fast, possessed of almost unlimited qualities of endurance and are armed with torpedoes and missiles. The T class, themselves an evolution of the patrol submarines of the First World War, mark the transition from the slow, submersible, torpedo-carrying gunboat to the nuclear-powered leviathans of today.

◄
HMS *Triumph*, one of the first submarines of the class, out of Portsmouth in May 1939 as the casing party secure for sea. (Wright and Logan)

HMS *Tiptoe*, the last T-class submarine in commission, has an escort of four Wasp helicopters as she pays off in 1969. The difference in appearance between *Triumph* and *Tiptoe* represents the transition in the role of the submarine from multi-purpose submersible gunboat to the sleek, fast submarine-hunter.

Proud bearer of a famous name: the Trafalgar-class nuclear-powered fleet submarine HMS *Turbulent*. At 5,208 tons displacement (dived) she is nearly four times the displacement of an 'original' T-class submarine and carries a mixed load of Mk 24 ASW Tigerfish torpedoes, mines and Sub-Harpoon missiles. Other famous T-boat names used in the new class are *Triumph*, *Torbay* and *Trenchant*. (MoD)

References and Notes

Abbreviations: NMM–National Maritime Museum; PRO–Public Record Office; RNSM–Royal Navy Submarine Museum

1. The 1,000-Ton Submarine

1. Captain George Villar, RN, 7 December 1934, foreword to his paper on British Submarine Design. RNSM A1934/5.
2. Ibid., p. 31.
3. Rear-Admiral (Submarines) to Admiralty, 9 January 1934, RNSM A1934/5.
4. Figures for designs 'A' and 'B' are from Ship's Cover No. 542, National Maritime Museum. Figures for Laurence's design are from RNSM A1934/5.
5. National Maritime Museum, Ship's Cover No. 542.
6. DNC to Rear-Admiral (Submarines), 22 June 1934. RNSM A1934/5.
7. Copies of the entire correspondence are preserved in RNSM A1934/5. I have not been able to trace the originals in the PRO.
8. Documents covering the development of the design are to be found in National Maritime Museum, Ship's Cover No. 542, PRO ADM.1/9378 Design of a Submarine of 1,000 tons; and RNSM A1935/13 Design of 1,000-ton submarine.
9. National Maritime Museum, Ship's Cover No. 542.
10. National Maritime Museum, Ship's Cover No. 542.
11. HMS *Triton*: First of Class Trials, 5 December 1938, National Maritime Museum, Ship's Cover No. 542.
12. Costs are taken from figures given in National Maritime Museum, Ship's Cover No. 542.
13. National Maritime Museum, Ship's Cover No. 542.
14. DNC's *Submarine War Experiences*, p. 402. Typescript copy in RNSM.
15. Vice-Admiral Sir Hugh Mackenzie to Author, 7 February 1989.
16. For a brief account of Hr Ms *Zwaardvis*' operations in the Indian Ocean and SW Pacific, *see* Naval Staff History *Submarines, Operations in Far Eastern Waters*, vol. 3, Admiralty 1956, pp. 57, 78, 89, 95, 114.

2. Hull, Superstructure and Propulsion

1. Modifications to T-Class Bridges. RNSM A1938/56.
2. DNC's *Submarine War Experiences*. Report of HMS *Trident*, page 13. Typescript copy in RNSM.
3. Decision to rebuild *Triumph* and *Thunderbolt* without the bow externals taken on 24 January 1940. National Maritime Museum, Ship's Cover No. 542.
4. HMS *Triton*: First of Class Trials, 5 December 1938. National Maritime Museum, Ship's Cover No. 542.
5. DNC's *Submarine War Experiences*. Report of HMS *Truant*, page 13. Typescript copy in RNSM.
6. DNC's *Submarine War Experiences*. Page 311. Typescript copy in RNSM.
7. MSS comments on Submarine War Experiences, p. 73. Unnumbered document in RNSM library.
8. DNC's *Submarine War Experiences*. Report of HMS *Torbay*, page 92. Typescript copy in RNSM.
9. Gus Britton to Author, 12 August 1989.
10. DNC's *Submarine War Experiences*. Comments on torpedo armament, page 317. Typescript copy in RNSM.
11. Minute by Constructor Commander A. J. Sims RCNC, 9 May 1942. RNSM A1941/31.
12. Ibid.
13. DNC's *Submarine War Experiences*. Comments on Depth Keeping and Seaworthiness. p. 346. Typescript copy in RNSM. The submarine in question was HMS *Tudor*.
14. *Records of Warship Construction 1939–45: The History of DNC Department*. Typescript document in the NMM Draught Room, p. 32.
15. A. J. Sims: British Submarine Design during the War 1939–45; *Transactions of the Institution of Naval Architects*; July 1947, vol. 89, No. 3.
16. Commander R. G. Raikes to Author, 10 July 1989.
17. DNC's *Submarine War Experiences*. Deep Dive Figures. Typescript copy in RNSM.
18. Naval Staff History, *Submarines, vol. 1, Operations in Home, Northern and Arctic Waters*. Admiralty 1953, *Triad*'s experience on p. 18, *Taku*'s on p. 95.
19. National Maritime Museum, Ship's Cover No. 542.
20. Captain John Coote to Author, 17 May 1989.
21. HMS *Triton*: First of Class Trials, 5 December 1938. National Maritime Museum, Ship's Cover No. 542.
22. Vice-Admiral Sir Anthony Troup 9 February 1989.
23. HMS *Triton*: First of Class Trials, 5 December 1938. National Maritime Museum, Ship's Cover No. 542.
24. Vice-Admiral Sir John Roxburgh to Author, 13 March 1989.
25. Admiral (Submarines) to Vice-Admiral Sir Neville Syfret, 14 March 1944. Letter in RNSM.
26. Vice-Admiral Sir John Roxburgh to Author, 13 March 1989.
27. Vice-Admiral Sir Hugh Mackenzie to Author, 7 February 1989.
28. Commander Arthur Pitt to Author, 12 May 1989.
29. Naval Staff History. *Submarines vol. 3, Operations in Far Eastern Waters*. Admiralty 1953, p. 30.
30. DNC's *Submarine War Experiences*. Report of HMS *Terrapin*, page 206. Typescript copy in RNSM.
31. DNC's *Submarine War Experiences*. Report of HMS *Triumph*, page 322. Typescript copy in RNSM.
32. DNC's *Submarine War Experiences*. Report of HMS *Talisman*, page 39. Typescript copy in RNSM.
33. DNC's *Submarine War Experiences*. Report of the Dutch boat, Hr Ms *Zwaardvis*, page 200. Typescript copy in RNSM.

3. Torpedoes, Guns and Mines

1. Detailed descriptions of the construction of the torpedo tubes and their associated tanks are contained in the *Specification for Building a Submarine of the T Class of the 1937 Programme*. HMSO, London. Copy in RNSM Library.
2. National Maritime Museum, Ship's Cover No. 542.
3. DNC's *Submarine War Experiences*. Report of HMS *Trident*, page 40. Typescript copy in RNSM Library.
4. Power Loading of torpedoes in HMS *Triumph*. RNSM A1977/56.
5. Ibid.
6. *Records of Warship Construction 1939–45: The History of DNC Department*. Typescript document in the NMM Draught Room, p. 13.
7. A drawing in the Admiralty collection of Ship's Plans at the NMM clearly shows *Triton*'s external tubes arranged horizontally.
8. Charles Deleay to Author, 11 August 1989.
9. HMS *Torbay*, Letter of Proceedings quoted in *Submarine General Letter* No. 185, section 9. Typescript copy in RNSM Library.
10. DNC's *Submarine War Experiences*. Report of HMS *Truant*, page 21. Typescript copy in RNSM Library.
11. HMS *Sidon* sunk at Portland on 16 June 1955 following the explosion of

a Mk XII in one of her torpedo tubes. After this accident and after a rogue Mk XII caused chaos on the Arrochar torpedo range, the weapon was withdrawn. See Anthony Preston: From Fancy to Stingray; British Torpedoes since 1945. *Warship No. 19.* Conway Maritime Press.

12. National Maritime Museum, Ship's Cover No. 778.
13. Constructor Commander A. C. Sims RCNC, 11 August 1943. RNSM.
14. HMS *Trident,* Letter of Proceedings quoted in *Submarine General Letter* No. 27, section 5. Typescript copy in RNSM Library.
15. G. Cuddon to Author, 4 December 1988
16. Report of a Visit to the Far East by Commander J. W. Maitland, gunnery officer on the staff of Admiral (Submarines) December 1944–January 1945. RNSM. A1944/20.
17. Constructor Commander A. C. Sims, 5 February 1942. RNSM.
18. W. A. Horton to Gus Britton, 28 January 1987.
19. G. Cuddon to Author, 4 December 1988.
20. Third Submarine Flotilla, Monthly General Letter, July 1945. Unnumbered copy in RNSM Library.
21. Report of a Visit to the Far East by Commander J. W. Maitland, gunnery officer on the staff of Admiral (Submarines) December 1944–January 1945. RNSM. A1944/20.
22. Ibid.
23. Admiral (Submarines) to Admiralty, 14 February 1945. RNSM.
24. HMS *Tetrarch*: Docking Plan. Admiralty Ships' Plans collection; NMM.
25. Minelaying Gear in T-Class Submarines. RNSM A1944/20.
26. Vice-Admiral Sir Max Horton to Admiralty, 28 February 1940. RNSM A1939/40.
27. For the full sorry story of the problems with *Tetrarch's* minelaying gear see DTM's interim report quoted in RNSM A1939/40.
28. Ibid.
29. Commander E. Gibson to Admiral (Submarines), 12 April 1940. RNSM A1939/20.
30. M Type G Mine, Handling and Discharge Trials in HMS *Talisman,* 6 July 1940. RNSM A1939/20.
31. M Mk II Mine Stowage Arrangements: *Submarine General Letter* No. 75, section 3. Typescript

copy in RNSM Library.
32. Naval Staff History, *British Mining Operations 1939–45,* London 1973, p. 691.

4. Sensors and Communications
1. *Handbook of Submarines,* vol 1, Admiralty, CB1795A 1943, pp. 31–3. Copy in RNSM Library.
2. Ibid.
3. DNC's *Submarine War Experiences.* Depth Keeping and Seaworthiness, p. 345. Typescript copy in RNSM Library.
4. *T-Class Submarine Conversion: Statement of Requirements.* Section 38: Periscopes. Typescript Copy in RNSM Library.
5. National Maritime Museum, Ships Cover No. 778.
6. Hackmann, Willem. *Seek and Strike: Sonar, Anti Submarine Warfare and the Royal Navy 1914–54.* HMSO London, 1984, pp. 216–17.
7. *Records of Warship Construction 1939–45: The History of the DNC Department.* Typescript document in NMM Draught Room, p. 14.
8. National Maritime Museum, Ships Cover No. 778.
9. Hackmann, Willem. *Seek and Strike: Sonar, Anti Submarine Warfare and the Royal Navy 1914–54.* HMSO London, 1984, pp. 352–3.
10. Ibid, but see also Grove, Eric, *Vanguard to Trident: British Naval Policy since WW2,* Bodley head 1987, p. 226. The author is also grateful to Lt-Cdr Michael Wilson for assistance in clarifying some of the details of 171.
11. Hackmann, Willem. *Seek and Strike: Sonar, Anti Submarine Warfare and the Royal Navy 1914–54.* HMSO London, 1984, pp. 352–3.
12. Captain John Coote to Author, 17 May 1989.
13. Friedmann, Norman. *Naval Radar.* Conway Maritime Press, p. 196.
14. DNC's *Submarine War Experiences.* Section on Masts, pp. 336–7. Typescript copy in RNSM Library.
15. Letters of Proceedings of HM Submarines *Taurus* and *Tactician* in *Submarine General Letter* No. 159 section 1. Typescript copy in RNSM Library.
16. Memorandum by W. Fitzgerald on the Development of Submarine Radar. RNSM A1944/55.
17. Commander R. G. Raikes to Author, 10 July 1989.
18. Experiences of HMS *Thorough* while

on patrol, May 1945. RNSM A1945/55.
19. The employment of Radar in Submarines, 3 July 1942. PRO ADM.1/12476.
20. Experiences of HMS *Thorough* while on patrol, May 1945. RNSM A1945/55.
21. Friedman, Norman. *Naval Radar,* Conway Maritime Press, p. Details of *Tiptoe's* SJ installation supplied by Commander G. Mellor DSC, 24 May 1989.
22. Naval Staff History. *Submarines vol. 3, Operations in Far Eastern Waters,* Admiralty 1956, p. 98.
23. Naval Staff History. *Submarines vol. 3, Operations in Far Eastern Waters,* Admiralty 1956, p. 110.
24. Friedman, Norman. *Naval Radar,* Conway Maritime Press, p. 191.
25. Vice-Admiral Sir John Roxburgh to Author, 13 March 1989.
26. Ibid.
27. Stevens, Captain J. S. *Never Volunteer: A Submariner's Scrapbook.* Solent Printers, Havant, 1971.
28. DNC's *Submarine War Experiences.* Section on Masts, pp. 336–7. Typescript copy in RNSM Library.
29. Friedman, Norman. *Naval Radar.* Conway Maritime Press, p. 191.
30. Captain John Coote to Author, 30 June 1989.
31. *Handbook of Submarines vol 1.* CB1795A 1943, p. 39. Copy in RNSM Library.
32. *Handbook of Submarines vol 1.* CB1795A 1943, p. 38. Copy in RNSM Library.
33. *Handbook of Submarines vol 1.* CB1795A 1943, p. 37. Copy in RNSM Library.
34. Hezlet, Vice-Admiral Sir Arthur. *The Electron and Sea Power.* Peter Davies 1975, p. 113.
35. *Handbook of Submarines vol 1.* CB1795A 1943, p. 37. Copy in RNSM Library.
36. *Handbook of Submarines vol 1.* CB1795A 1943, p. 37. Copy in RNSM Library.
37. *T Class Submarine Conversion: Statement of Requirements.* Section 31, W/T and A/S Machinery. Typescript copy in RNSM Library.
38. National Maritime Museum, Ship's cover 778.

5. Life Below
1. Staff Requirement for a 1,000 ton Submarine. RNSM A1935/13.
2. Scheme of complement from Ship's Cover 542, NMM.

3. Ron Slade to Author, 9 January 1989.
4. Commander Arthur Pitt to Author, 12 May 1989.
5. Lieutenant-Commander Roy Foster to Gus Britton, 25 August 1987.
6. Charles Deleay to Author, 11 August 1988.
7. Slade, op. cit.
8. R. Jones to Author, 28 September 1988.
9. DNC's *Submarine War Experiences*. Refrigeration and Cold Storage, p. 300. Typescript copy in RNSM Library.
10. DNC's *Submarine War Experiences*. Endurance Figures for HMS *Tantalus*, p. 421. Typescript copy in RNSM Library. These figures refer to *fresh* provisions only.
11. Vice-Admiral Sir Hugh Mackenzie to Author, 7 February 1989.
12. Stan Law to Author, 1 August 1988.
13. J. K. Chapman to Author, 2 September 1988.
14. T. J. Soar to Author, 14 November 1988.
15. Chapman, op. cit.
16. DNC's *Submarine War Experiences*. Remarks of HMS *Torbay* on patrol from 2 to 22 August 1941, p. 74. Typescript copy in RNSM Library. It should be pointed out that for the last three days of the patrol *Torbay* was carrying an additional 130 people onboard: soldiers evacuated from Crete.
17. DNC's *Submarine War Experiences*. Remarks of HMS *Triumph* on patrol from 19 August to 2 September 1941, p. 77. Typescript copy in RNSM Library.
18. Letter of Proceedings of HMS *Tuna*. Submarine General Letter No. 27, section 2. Typescript copy in RNSM Library.
19. Lt-Cdr R. M. Favell in HMS *Trespasser*, January 1944.
20. King, Cdr. W. D. A. *Dive and Attack: A Submariner's Story*, William Kimber 1983, see chapters 15–18 for an account of *Trusty*'s ordeal in the Far East.
21. DNC's *Submarine War Experiences*. Remarks of HMS *Templar* on patrol carried out between 9 and 31 October 1943, p. 174. Typescript copy in RNSM Library.
22. DNC's *Submarine War Experiences*. Remarks of HMS *Trespasser* on patrol carried out between 10 November and 3 December 1943, p. 176. Typescript copy in RNSM Library.
23. DNC's *Submarine War Experiences*. Refrigeration and Cold Storage, p. 300. Typescript copy in RNSM Library.
24. Charles Deleay to Author, 11 August 1988.
25. Medical Log of HMS *Terrapin* compiled by CPO Mallett DSM**. HMS *Terrapin* file, RNSM.
26. Ibid.
27. King, Commander W. D. A. *Dive and Attack: A Submariner's Story*, William Kimber, 1983, p. 205.
28. Mars, Alistair. *HMS Thule Intercepts*, Elek Books 1956, pp. 54–62.
29. Scheme of Complement for a T Conversion from Ship's Cover 778, National Maritime Museum.
30. *T-Class Submarine Conversion: Statement of Requirements*. Section 34 Air Conditioning. Typescript copy in RNSM Library.
31. Captain John Coote to Author, 17 May 1989.
32. Captain John Coote to Author, 17 May 1989.

6. War 1939–45; Worth Their Weight in Gold

1. Evans, A. S. *Beneath the Waves*, William Kimber 1986, pp. 195–9. See also naval Staff History, *Submarines vol. 1, Operations in Home, Northern and Atlantic Waters*, Admiralty 1953, p. 14. The three volumes of the Naval Staff History dealing with submarine operations during the Second World War are strongly recommended.
2. DNC's *Submarine War Experiences*. Report of HMS *Triumph*, p. 14–16. Typescript copy in RNSM Library. Also Stevens, Captain J. S., *Never Volunteer: A Submariner's Scrapbook*, Solent Press, pp. 13–15.
3. Naval Staff History, *Submarines vol. 1, Operations in Home, Northern and Atlantic Waters*, Admiralty 1953, pp. 30–33.
4. Naval Staff History, *Submarines, vol. 1, Operations in Home, Northern and Atlantic Waters*, Admiralty 1953, p. 32.
5. DNC's *Submarine War Experiences*. Report of HMS *Tetrarch*, pp. 22–3. Typescript copy in RNSM Library. Also Mills, Captain R. G. St. George's Day, *Blackwood's Magazine*, January 1959, Number 1719, Volume 285, pp. 1–13.
6. Evans, A. S. *Beneath the Waves*, William Kimber 1984, p. 195 et seq.
7. Naval Staff History, *Submarines vol, 1, Operations in Home, Northern and Atlantic Waters*, Admiralty 1953, p. 201. Commander A. J. Pitt to Author, 12 May 1989.
8. Vice Admiral Sir Hugh Mackenzie to Author, 7 February 1989.
9. Naval Staff History, *Submarines vol. 2, Operations in the Mediterranean*, Admiralty 1955, p. 29.
10. Naval Staff History, *Submarines vol. 2, Operations in the Mediterranean*, Admiralty 1955, p. 26.
11. The author is grateful to Anthony Cleminson Esq. for supplying a translation of the official Italian account of this action.
12. Naval Staff History, *Submarines vol. 2, Operations in the Mediterranean*, Admiralty 1955, p. 76. See also Chapman, Paul, *Submarine Torbay*, Robert Hale 1989, pp. 130–40 and Lipscombe, Cdr. F. W., *The British Submarine*, Conway Maritime Press 1975, p. 108.
13. Naval Staff History, *Submarines vol. 2, Operations in the Mediterranean*, Admiralty 1955, p. 49.
14. Naval Staff History, *Submarines vol. 2, Operations in the Mediterranean*, Admiralty 1955, p. 112. Comment refers to the sinking of *Porfido* by *Tigris*.
15. Personal information supplied to the Author.
16. Vice-Admiral Sir Hugh Mackenzie to Author, 7 February 1989.
17. Vice-Admiral Sir Hugh Mackenzie to Author, 7 February 1989.
18. DNC's *Submarine War Experiences*. Report of HMS *Thrasher*, p. 106–8. Typescript copy in RNSM Library.
19. Vice-Admiral Sir Hugh Mackenzie to Author, 7 February 1989.
20. Captain S.1 to CinC Mediterranean 7 January 1941. The Author is grateful to Bob Coppock of the Naval Historical Branch at the Ministry of Defence for information on *Triad*'s loss.
21. Naval Staff History, *Submarines vol. 2, Operations in the Mediterranean*, Admiralty 1955, p. 122.
22. Vice-Admiral Sir Hugh Mackenzie to Author, 7 February 1989.
23. Amm. Di Div Vitaliano Rauber. *La Lotta Antisommergibile*, volume XXII of *La Martina Italiana Nella Seconda Guerra Mondiale*, Ufficio Storico Della Marina Militare, Rome 1978, pp. 280–7. Captain S.8 to CinC Mediterranean, 23 March 1943, PRO ADM.199/1848. Evans, A. S. *Beneath the Waves*, William Kimber 1984, p. 337–40. Also comments by Vice-Admiral Sir Anthony Troup to Author, 9 February 1989.
24. Naval Staff History. *Submarines vol. 2, Operations in the Mediterranean*, Admiralty, 1955, p. 61.

7. Submarines or Gunboats?

1. HMS *Tally-Ho*: Report of Proceedings quoted in Trenowden, Ian, *The Hunting Submarine; The Fighting Life of HMS Tally-Ho*, William Kimber 1974, p. 88.
2. DNC's *Submarine War Experiences*, Report of HMS *Tally-Ho*, p. 188. Typescript copy in RNSM Library.
3. Naval Staff History, *British Mining Operations 1939–45*, London 1973, p. 691–730.
4. Naval Staff History, *Submarines vol. 3, Operations in Far Eastern Waters*, Admiralty 1956, p. 71.
5. Op. Cit., p. 107.
6. Op. Cit., p. 78. Register of the *Militaire Willems Orde (MWO)* p. 222.
7. Vice-Admiral Sir Hugh Mackenzie to Author, 7 February 1989.
8. DNC's *Submarine War Experiences*. Endurance Figures for HMS *Tantalus*, p. 421. Typescript copy in RNSM Library.
9. Naval Staff History, *Submarines*

vol. 3, *Operations in Far Eastern Waters*, Admiralty 1956, pp. 101–5. See also Winton, J., *The Forgotten Fleet*, Michael Joseph 1969, pp. 237–68.

10. DNC's *Submarine War Experiences*. Report of HMS *Terrapin*, pp. 206–9. Typescript copy in RNSM Library. George Cuddon to Author, 4 December 1988.

11. Naval Staff History, *Submarines* vol. 3, *Operations in Far Eastern Waters*, Admiralty 1956, p. 100.

12. *The Attack on the Tirpitz by Midget Submarines: Operation Source, 22 September 1943*. BR.1736(22), Admiralty 1948. See also Richard Compton-Hall, *Submarine Warfare: Monsters and Midgets*, Blandford 1985, pp. 127–43.

13. Naval Staff History, *Submarines* vol. 2, *Operations in the Mediterranean*, Admiralty 1955, pp. 118–19.

14. Naval Staff History, *Submarines* vol. 3, *Operations in Far Eastern Waters*, Admiralty 1956, p. 51, 57. Cruikshank, G. *SOE in the Far East*, Oxford University Press 1983, p. 30.

15. Simpson, Rear-Admiral G. W. G. *Periscope View: A Professional Autobiography*. Macmillan 1972, pp. 114–5.

16. The submarine aspects of this operation are not well documented in official records. The best account is in Chapman Paul, *Submarine Torbay*, Robert Hale 1989, pp. 85–95.

17. Cruikshank, G. *SOE in the Far East*, Oxford University Press 1983, P. 144.

18. Op. Cit., p. 252.

8. The Admiralty Regrets

1. Statement of the First Lord of the Admiralty, 12 March 1934. Printed as Appendix 2 in the *Report of Admiral Nasmith's Committee on the Methods of Saving Life in Sunken Submarines*, September 1939.

2. Minute by Director of Plans, November 1934. PRO ADM.1/9373.

3. Tabb, H. J. Escape from Submarines: A Short Historical Review of Policy and Equipment in the Royal Navy. *Transactions of the Royal Institute of Naval Architects*, 1974, p. 31.

4. The full *Thetis* casualty list is given in Warren, C. E. T. and Benson, James. *The Admiralty Regrets*, Harrap, 1958, pp. 243–5. The *Report of the Tribunal of Enquiry into the Loss of HMS Thetis*, HMSO 1940, is also required reading for anyone seriously interested in the story of HMS *Thetis*.

5. The *Report of the Tribunal of Enquiry into the Loss of HMS Thetis*, HMSO 1940, p. 50.

6. The *Report of the Tribunal of Enquiry into the Loss of HMS Thetis*, HMSO 1940, p. 29.

7. MSS notes by Warrant Engineer Roy Glenn, Engineer Officer of HMS *Thetis*, reproduced as photographs in Warren, C. E. T. and Benson, James, *The Admiralty Regrets*, Harrap 1958, pp. 60–1.

8. The reconstruction of events in HMS *Thetis* after the escape of Arnold and Shaw is based on the examination of the hull after *Thetis* had been salved. See The *Report of the Tribunal of Enquiry into the Loss of HMS Thetis*, HMSO 1940, pp. 39–43. That the cause of death was asphyxia rather than drowning was confirmed during a full necropsy on two of *Thetis* ship's company performed by Surgeon Commander G. Rainsford, see PRO ADM.1/4429.

9. *Report of Admiral Nasmith's Committee on the Methods of Saving Life in Sunken Submarines*, September 1939.

10. National Maritime Museum, Ship's Cover No. 542.

11. HMS *Truant*: general file; RNSM Library.

12. Shelford, Captain W. O. *Subsunk! The Story of Submarine Escape*. Harrap, 1960. Details of the conning tower escape route are in an unnumbered document in RNSM Library.

13. Evans, A. S. *Beneath the Waves*, William Kimber 1984, pp. 393–400.

14. Citation from the *London Gazette*, quoted in Evans op. cit., pp. 399–400.

15. *History of Submarine Escape*. Anonymous unnumbered paper in RNSM Library.

16. Bernard, Surgeon Commander E. E. P. 100 years of Underwater Escape, *Proceedings of the Royal Society of Medicine*. SE(B), 73, 13, 1971/1972.

17. Information surrounding the loss of the Israeli submarine *Dakar* is hard to come by. The best account is Israeli Navy Submarines in *Defence Update International* No. 56.

9. Toward the Killer Submarine

1. *Pink List* (Daily Movements of HM Ships) 2 September 1945. Naval Historical Branch, Ministry of Defence.

2. Third Submarine Flotilla, Monthly General Letter, July 1945. Unnumbered copy in RNSM Library.

3. *Pink List* (Daily Movements of HM Ships) 31 December 1948. Naval Historical Branch, Ministry of Defence.

4. *Submarine General Letter* 21 September 1948, RNSM A1949.

5. Naval Staff History, *British and Commonwealth Naval Operations in Korea 1950–3*, Admiralty 1967, p. 264.

6. King, Cdr. W. D. A. *Dive and Attack: A Submariner's Story*, William Kimber 1983, p. 109.

7. Fitting of Schnorckel in HM Submarines, PRO ADM.1/16396.

8. *Truant's* submerged passage using 'Snort', RNSM 1946/22.

9. Personal information supplied to the Author.

10. HM Submarine *Tally-Ho*: Submerged Passage of the Atlantic; Exercise 'Snortlant 1'. PRO ADM.1/25557.

11. Shelford, Captain W. O. *Subsunk! The Story of Submarine Escape*. Harrap,

1960.

12. Stevens, Captain J. S. *Never Volunteer: A Submariner's Scrapbook*, p. 73.

13. Ibid.

14. Captain John Coote to Author, 17 May 1989.

15. *Submarine General Letter* March 1949, RNSM A1949.

16. Ron Slade to Author, 9 January 1989.

17. *Submarine General Letter* 30 June 1950, RNSM A1949.

18. Captain John Coote to Author, 17 May 1989.

19. *Submarine General Letter* 20 September 1950. RNSM A1949, Also comments by Captain John Coote and Commander Tony Bagley to Author on 17 May and 16 August 1989.

20. A Balanced Postwar Fleet: PRO ADM.205/53.

21. For details on the priority given to ASW see ADM M/TASW 289/47 in PRO ADM.1/25252. Other quotes are from ADM.205/53.

22. Full details of *Tradewind's* conversion and first of class trials are in RNSM B1944/6.

23. Grove, Eric, *Vanguard to Trident: British Naval Policy since WW2*, Bodley Head 1987, p. 223.

24. Naval Staff History, *Submarines* vol. 1, *Operations in Home, Northern and Atlantic Waters*, Admiralty 1953, p. 223.

25. *Submarine General Letter* 15 March 1950, RNSM A1949. See also Grove, Eric, *Vanguard to Trident: British Naval Policy since WW2*, Bodley Head 1987, p. 22–4.

26. *Submarine General Letter* 20 September 1950, RNSM A1949.

27. *Submarine General Letter* 20 September 1950, RNSM A1949.

28. Personal information supplied to the Author.

29. Minute by Admiral (Submarines), 17 July 1945, paragraphs 15, 16 and 19 apply. PRO ADM.1/20045.

10. The Fast Submarine

1. National Maritime Museum, Ship's cover 778.

2. Ibid.

3. Staff Requirement for a T-Class Conversion. National Maritime Museum Ship's Cover 778.

4. T-Class Conversion: Statement of Requirements. Typescript copy in RNSM Library.

5. HMS *Taciturn*, First of Class Trials. National Maritime Museum Ship's Cover 778.

6. Captain John Coote to Author, 17 May 1989.

7. Bryant to DNC, 13 October 1951. National Maritime Museum Ship's Cover 778.

8. Ibid.

9. Note by Lt.-Cdr, J. C. Y. Roxburgh. National Maritime Museum Ship's Cover 778.

10. Captain John Coote to Author, 17 May 1989.

11. Captain John Coote to Author, 17 May 1989.
12. *Taciturn's* account of her experiences off Jan Mayen Island is from National Maritime Museum Ship's cover 778.
13. *Submarine Periodical Letter*, 1 December 1950, para 48. RNSM A1949.
14. *Tireless* vs. *Tudor* Trials. RNSM B1953/1.
15. Ibid.
16. Ibid.
17. Sabotage in HMS *Tapir*, PRO ADM.1/ 25743. The enquiring researcher will have to wait until 2029 when the file is released to discover what happened in *Tapir*.
18. Details of the accident which befell HMS *Talent* can be found in the Court of Enquiry report in PRO ADM.1/ 25305. Supplementary information is also available in RNSM A1981/48 and in HMS *Talent's* general file.
19. HMS *Taciturn* general file, RNSM.
20. HMS *Turpin's* Long Tow, RNSM A1958/2.
21. Torpedo Accident in HMS *Trump*, RNSM A1977/49.
22. Friedman, N., Project 'Guppy', *Warship*, No. 9, Conway Maritime Press, 1979.
23. Information on the fates of the various T-class submarines comes from records at Naval Historical Branch, Ministry of Defence. See also Colledge, *Ships of the Royal Navy, An Historical Index*, vol. 1, David and Charles 1969 together with the *Supplement* by the same author published by the World Ship Society in 1986.

11. In Retrospect
1. Brown, D. K., *What is a 'Good Design'?*, unpublished typescript paper.

◀
HMS *Tribune* coming alongside the depot ship HMS *Forth* in Holy Loch in 1940.

Appendixes

1. List of T-class submarines and their fates

Group One Boats

Triton (N.15): Vickers Armstrong 5 October 1937, lost in the southern Adriatic, cause unknown, on or about 6 December 1940.

Thetis (11.T): Cammell Laird 29 June 1938, sunk on trials 1 June 1939, salved and renamed Thunderbolt (N.25), depth-charged off Cape San Vito by Italian corvette *Cicogna* 14 March 1943.

Tribune (N.76): Scotts 8 December 1938, arrived Milford Haven for breaking up July 1947.

Trident (N.52): Cammell Laird 7 December 1938, arrived Newport for breaking up February 1946.

Triumph (N.18): Vickers Armstrong 16 February 1938, presumed mined in the Cyclades on or about 31 December 1941.

Taku (N.38): Cammell Laird 20 May 1939, sold November 1946 for breaking up at Llanelly.

Tarpon (N.17): Scotts 17 October 1939, sunk in North Sea by German Q ship, *Schiff 40* 10 April 1940.

Thistle (N.24): Vickers Armstrong 25 October 1938, torpedoed in North Sea by U4 10 April 1940.

Tigris (N.63): HM Dockyard Chatham 31 October 1939, depth-charged by the German *UJ2210* SE of Capri 27 February 1943.

Triad (N.53): Vickers Armstrong 5 May 1939, sunk by gunfire and torpedo by the Italian S/M *Enrico Toti* 15 October 1940.

Truant (N.68): Vickers Armstrong 5 May 1939, sold for breaking up 19 December 1945, wrecked December 1946 while under tow to Briton Ferry.

Tuna (N.94): Scotts 10 May 1940, sold 19 December 1945, arrived Briton Ferry for breaking up 24 June 1946.

Talisman (N.78): Cammell Laird 29 January 1940, presumed mined south of Sicily on or about 17 September 1942.

Tetrarch (N.77): Vickers Armstrong 14 November 1939, presumed mined in Sicilian Channel to the SW of Sicily 27 October 1941 or off Cavoli Island 29 October 1941.

Torbay (N.79): HM Dockyard Chatham 9 April 1940, sold 19 December 1945, broken up at Briton Ferry.

Group Two Boats

Tempest (N.86): Cammell Laird 10 June 1941, depth-charged in Gulf of Taranto by Italian corvette *Circe* 13 February 1942.

Thorn (N.11): Cammell Laird 18 March 1941, depth-charged off Gavdo Island by Italian DE *Pegaso* 7 August 1942.

Thrasher (N.37): Cammell Laird 28 November 1940, arrived 9 March 1947 for breaking up at Briton Ferry.

Traveller (N.48): Scotts 27 August 1941, presumed mined in Gulf of Taranto on or about 4 December 1942.

Trooper (N.91): Scotts 5 March 1942, presumed mined east of Leros, eastern Aegean, on or about 10 October 1943.

Trusty (N.45): Vickers Armstrong 14 March 1941, arrived Milford Haven for breaking up 4 January 1947.

Turbulent (N.98): Vickers Armstrong 12 May 1941, presumed sunk by depth-charges from Italian trawler *Teti II* off Bastia 12 March 1943.

Group Three Boats

P.311: Vickers Armstrong 5 March 1942, presumed mined off Maddalena on or about 2 January 1943.

Tactician (P.314): Vickers Armstrong 29 July 1942, arrived Newport for breaking up 6 December 1963.

Tally-Ho (P.317): Vickers Armstrong 23 December 1942, arrived Briton Ferry for breaking up 10 February 1967.

Tantalus (P.318): Vickers Armstrong 24 February 1943, broken up at Milford Haven from November 1950.

Tantivy (P.319): Vickers Armstrong 6 April 1943, expended as A/S target Cromarty Firth 1951.

Taurus (P.339): Vickers Armstrong 27 June 1942, broken up at Dunston from April 1960.

Templar (P.316): Vickers Armstrong 26 October 1942, sunk as ASDIC target in 1950, raised 4 December 1958, arrived at

Troon for breaking up 17 July 1959.

Trespasser (P.312): Vickers Armstrong 29 May 1942, arrived Gateshead for breaking up 26 September 1961.

Truculent (P.315): Vickers Armstrong 12 September 1942, sunk in collision with MV *Divina* off the Nore 12 January 1950, raised and sold 8 May 1950, broken up at Grays.

Taciturn (P.334): Vickers Armstrong 7 June 1944, sold to T. W. Ward 23 July 1971, arrived Briton Ferry for breaking up 8 August 1971.

Talent (1) (P.322): Vickers Armstrong 17 July 1943, to Netherlands and renamed *Zwaardvis*, sold for breaking up 12 July 1963.

Tasman (P.337): Vickers Armstrong 13 February 1945, renamed *Talent* April 1945, sold for breaking up 1969.

Tapir (P.335): Vickers Armstrong 21 August 1944, arrived Faslane for breaking up 4 December 1966.

Tarn (P.336): Vickers Armstrong 19 June 1943, to Netherlands and renamed *Tijgerhaai*, sold for breaking up 5 November 1965.

Telemachus (P.321): Vickers Armstrong 19 June 1943, arrived Charlestown for breaking up 28 August 1961.

Teredo (P.338): Vickers Armstrong 27 April 1945, arrived Faslane for breaking up 1 February 1966.

Terrapin (P.323): Vickers Armstrong 31 August 1943, damaged in Japanese DC attack 19 May 1945, arrived Troon for breaking up June 1946.

Thorough (P.324): Vickers Armstrong 30 October 1943, arrived at Dunston for breaking up 29 June 1961.

Thule (P.325): HM Dockyard Devonport 22 October 1942, arrived Inverkeithing for breaking up 14 September 1962.

Tiptoe (P.332): Vickers Armstrong 25 February 1944, sold Pound of Portsmouth for breaking up 16 April 1971. After portion extant as of 1989.

Tireless (P.327): HM Dockyard Portsmouth 19 March 1943, arrived Newport for breaking up 20 September 1968.

Token (P.328): HM Dockyard Portsmouth 19 March 1943, arrived at Cairnryan for breaking up March 1970.

Tradewind (P.329): HM Dockyard Chatham 11 December 1942, arrived at Charlestown for breaking up 14 December 1955.

Trenchant (P.331): HM Dockyard Chatham 24 March 1943, arrived Faslane for breaking up 23 July 1963.

Trump (P.333): Vickers Armstrong 25 March 1944, arrived at Newport for breaking up August 1971.

Tudor (P.326): HM Dockyard Devonport 23 September 1942, arrived at Faslane for breaking up 23 July 1963.

Tabard (P.342): Scotts ex-Vickers Armstrong 21 November 1945, sold 2 January 1974, arrived Newport for breaking up 14 March 1974.

Thermopylae (P.355): HM Dockyard Chatham 27 June 1945, scuttled in Loch Striven for exercise and subsequently raised, sold 26 May 1970, arrived Troon for breaking up 3 July 1970.

Totem (P.352): HM Dockyard Devonport 28 September 1943, to Israel 1965 and renamed *Dakar*, lost at sea on or about 25 January 1968.

Truncheon (P.353): HM Dockyard Devonport 22 February 1944, to Israel and renamed *Dolphin* for disposal 1977.

Turpin (P.354): HM Dockyard Chatham 5 August 1944, to Israel and renamed *Leviathan* for disposal 1977.

Thor (P.349): HM Dockyard Portsmouth 18 April 1944, cancelled 29 October 1945.

Tiara (P.351): HM Dockyard Portsmouth, cancelled 29 October 1945.

Theban (P.341): Vickers Armstrong, cancelled 29 october 1945.

Threat (P.344): Vickers Armstrong, cancelled 29 October 1945.

Talent (II): Scotts ex-Vickers Armstrong, cancelled 29 October 1945.

2. Weapons

Torpedoes

21-inch Mark VIII
Length: 21 feet 7 inches
Total weight: 3,452lb max.
Negative Buoyancy: 804lb max.
Volume (air vessel): 15.64 cu. ft.
Pressure: 2,500psi, 3,000psi in Mk VIII**
HP at 40 knots: 230 in Mk VIII, 322 in Mk VIII**
Range: 5,000 yards at 40 knots (45.5 knots in Mk VIII**), 7,000 yards at 41 knots
Warhead: 750lb TNT in Mk VIII, 805lb Torpex in Mk VIII**
Other variants include the Mk VIII*E (for use in external tubes) which had smaller propellers and lacked the 45.5 knot speed setting of the Mk VIII**.

21-inch Mk XII 'Fancy'
21-inch high-speed HTP-driven torpedo using ᵃ modified Mk VIII body.
Withdrawn after *Sidon* disaster.

21-inch Mk XXS 'Bidder'
21-inch electrically driven passive homing torpedo. Full specification unavailable.

21-inch Mk XXIII Torpedo
21-inch electrically driven wire-guided torpedo. Ex- 'Grog' and 'Mackle': wire-guided version of Mk XX. Full specification unavailable.

Guns

4-inch QF Mk XII and XXII on S1 Mounting
Bore: 4 inches
Breech mechanism: horizontal sliding block
Weight incl BM: 1.297 tons
Length oa: 165.4 inches
Length of bore: 160 inches
Length of rifling: 138.175 inches
Twist: uniform 1 in 25 calibres
Weight of shell: 35lb
Weight of charge: 4.578lb of NF059
Muzzle velocity: 1,873fps
Max. range: 10,450 yards at 20° elevation
Elevation: +20° to −3°
Recoil: 36 inches

4-inch QF Mk XXIII on S2 Mounting
Bore: 4 inches
Breech mechanism: horizontal sliding block
Weight incl. BM: 14cwt 0qtr 1lb
Length oa: 137.56 inches
Length of bore: 132.16 inches
Length of rifling: 116.58 inches
Twist: uniform 1 in 25 calibres
Weight of shell: 35lb 13oz
Weight of charge: 3lb 12oz
Muzzle velocity: 1,750fps
Max. range: 10,450 yards at 20° elevation
Elevation: +30° to −10°
Recoil: 24 inches

20mm Oerlikon
Bore: 20mm
Weight of gun: 141–150lb depending on Mk
Weight of barrel: 48lb
Length: 87 inches
Length of bore: 55.118 inches
Length of rifling: 49.061 inches
Twist: uniform 1 in 36 calibres
Weight of shell: 0.272lb
Weight of charge: 0.0628lb NC Flake
Muzzle velocity: 2,750fps
Max. range: 4,800 yards
Ceiling: 10,000 feet
Mountings used in submarines were the Mk IIA S/M and the Mk VIIA S/M. HMS *Tireless* had a twin Mk XIIA S/M mounting.

Mines

21-inch M Mk II Torpedo Tude Laid Mine
Diameter: 21 inches
Length oa: 96 inches
Length of body: 73 inches
Weight: 1,800lb
Displacement in sea water: 960lb
Weight of charge:
   Minol 1,060lb
   Amatol 1,000lb

3. Axis Warships and Merchant Shipping Sunk by T-Class Submarines 1939–45

This table lists the ships of more than 500 tons sunk or damaged by T-boats during the Second World War and whose loss had been confirmed by post-war examination of Axis records. Many T-boats amassed far higher totals of shipping sunk than listed here, by sinking small craft in the Mediterranean and the Far East about which accurate records are not available.

Abbreviations: MV–Merchant Vessel, EV–Escort Vessel, UB–U-Boat, D–Destroyer, TB–Torpedo-Boat, SV–Sailing Vessel, Aux–Naval Auxiliary, ML–Minelayer, H–Home Waters, M–Mediterranean, FE–Far East, *B–Beached, *CTL–Constructive Total Loss, *D–Damaged, *M–Minelay.

**Torbay's floating dock was the largest single target sunk by a T boat.

Date	Submarine	Enemy	Type	Tonnage	Theatre
1940					
8 April	Trident	Posidonia	tanker	8,100	H
9 April	Truant	Karlsruhe	cruiser	6,650	H
10 April	Triton	Friedenau	MV	5,219	H
		Wigbert	MV	3,648	H
		R.6	EV	354	H
11 April	Triad	Iona	MV	3,102	H
20 April	Triad	unknown	MV	4,400	H
2 May	Trident	Clare			
		Stinnes	MV	5,000	H *D
23 May	Truant	Preussen	MV	8,320	H
16 June	Tetrarch	Samland	tanker	5,978	H
2 Sept	Tigris	trawler	EV	600	H
22 Sept	Truant	Provvidenza	MV	8,460	M
22 Sept	Tuna	Tiranna	MV	7,320	H
24 Sept	Tuna	Ostmark	MV	1,280	H
4 Oct	Triton	F. Fassio	MV	1,860	M
2 Nov	Taku	Gedania	tanker	8,923	H
13 Nov	Tigris	Ch. Edmond	SV	301	H
13 Dec	Truant	S. Bianchi	MV	1,545	M
15 Dec	Thunderbolt	Tarantini	UB	1,031	H
16 Dec	Truant	Bonzo	tanker	8,175	M
18 Dec	Tuna	unknown	tug	250	H
1941					
3 Feb	Truant	Multedo	MV	1,130	M
12 Feb	Tigris	unknown	MV	1,200	H
19 Feb	Tigris	Guilvinec	MV	3,222	H
5 Mar	Triumph	Marzamemi	MV	960	M
5 Mar	Triumph	C Lo Faro	MV	900	M
3 April	Tigris	Thorn	tanker	5,485	H
12 April	Tetrarch	Persiano	tanker	2,475	M
? April	Truant	Prometeo	Aux	1,080	M *B
6 May	Truant	Bengasi	MV	1,715	M
6 May	Taku	Cagliari	MV	2,320	M
18 May	Tetrarch	Giovenezza	MV	2,360	M
6 June	Torbay	Alberta	tanker	3,360	M
10 June	Torbay	G. Ghirardi	tanker	3,320	M
11 June	Taku	Tilly Russ	MV	1,600	M
12 June	Taku	S. Scaroni	MV	1,365	M
27 June	Triumph	Salpa	UB	650	M
2 July	Torbay	C. D. Tripoli	MV	2,935	M
5 July	Tigris	M. Bianchi	UB	1,195	H
5 July	Torbay	Jantina	UB	650	M
10 July	Torbay	Strombo	tanker	5,230	M *CTL
13 July	Taku	Caldea	MV	2,705	M
7 Aug	Tigris	Haakon			
		Jarl	MV	1,482	H
22 Aug	Trident	Ostpreussen	MV	3,030	H
26 Aug	Triumph	Bolzano	cruiser	11,065	M *D
30 Aug	Trident	Dona II	MV	3,000	H
7 Sept	Thunderbolt	Sirena	MV	975	M
11 Sept	Thunderbolt	Livorno	MV	1,830	M

Date	Submarine	Enemy	Type	Tonnage	Theatre
13 Sept	Tigris	unknown	MV	2,000	H
17 Sept	Tigris	unknown	MV	2,000	H
23 Sept	Triumph	Luwsee	MV	2,370	M
27 Sept	Tetrarch	C. d. Bastia	MV	2,500	M
27 Sept	Trident	unknown	MV	1,000	H
4 Oct	Talisman	T. Gautier	liner	8,195	M
8 Oct	Trident	U31	UB	500	H *D
14 Oct	Tigris	unknown	MV	5,000	H
14 Oct	Tigris	unknown	MV	3,000	H
23 Oct	Truant	Virginia S	MV	3,885	M
25 Oct	Triumph	Monrosa	MV	6,705	M
31 Oct	Truant	Meteor	tanker	1,685	M
3 Nov	Trident	UJ1213	EV	750	H
7 Nov	Trident	unknown	MV	2,000	H *D
24 Nov	Triumph	Hercules	tug	630	M
25 Nov	Thrasher	Attilo Deffenu	MV	3,510	M
4 Dec	Trusty	Eridano	MV	3,585	M
11 Dec	Truant	Alcione	TB	679	M
11 Dec	Talisman	Calitea	MV	4,015	M
30 Dec	Thorn	Campina	tanker	3,030	M
1942					
10 Jan	Thrasher	Fedora	MV	5,015	M
28 Jan	Thorn	Ninuccia	MV	4,585	M
30 Jan	Thorn	Medusa	UB	650	M
1 Feb	Thunderbolt	Absirtea	MV	4,170	M
23 Feb	Trident	Prinz Eugen	cruiser	15,700	H *D
5 Mar	Torbay	Maddalena G.	MV	5,210	M
1 April	Truant	Yae Maru	MV	6,781	FE
1 April	Truant	Shunsei Maru	MV	4,939	FE
9 April	Thrasher	Gala	MV	1,030	M
13 April	Thrasher	Atlas	MV	2,300	M
16 April	Turbulent	Delia	MV	5,405	M
18 April	Torbay	Bellona	MV	1,295	M
20 April	Trident	Hoedur	MV	5,368	H
18 May	Turbulent	Bolsena	MV	2,385	M
19 May	Thrasher	Penelope	MV	1,160	M
29 May	Turbulent	Capo Arma	MV	3,170	M
29 May	Turbulent	Pessagno	D	1,900	M
4 June	Trusty	Toyohashi Maru	MV	7,031	FE
23 June	Thrasher	S. Antonio	MV	1,480	M
24 June	Turbulent	Regulus	MV	1,085	M
29 June	Thrasher	Diana	Aux	1,570	M
3 Aug	Thorn	Monviso	MV	5,320	M
4 Sept	Thrasher	Padenna	MV	1,590	M
5 Sept	Traveller	Albachirar	MV	1,245	M
8 Oct	Turbulent	Kreta	MV	2,360	M
20 Oct	Thrasher	Lero	MV	1,980	M
26 Oct	Taku	Arca	tanker	2,240	M
11 Nov	Turbulent	Benghazi	Aux	1,555	M
6 Dec	Tigris	Porfido	UB	697	M
14 Dec	Taku	Delfin	MV	5,230	M

153

Date	Submarine	Enemy	Type	Tonnage	Theatre
29 Dec	Turbulent	Marte	MV	5,290	M
1943					
11 Jan	Turbulent	V. Beraldo	MV	545	M
11 Jan	Tribune	Dalny	MV	6,670	M
21 Jan	Tigris	C. d. Genova	MV	5,415	M
1 Feb	Turbulent	Pozzuoli	MV	5,345	M
5 Feb	Turbulent	Utilitas	tanker	5,340	M
11 Feb	Torbay	Grete	MV	1,565	M
26 Feb	Torbay	Astigarraga	MV	3,560	M
28 Feb	Torbay	Ischia	MV	5,100	M
1 Mar	Turbulent	San Vincenzo	MV	865	M
6 Mar	Taurus	Bartolo	MV	3,120	M
10 Mar	Taurus	Derna	MV	1,770	M
10 Mar	Trooper	Rosario	tanker	5,470	M
12 Mar	Thunderbolt	Esterel	MV	3,100	M
17 Mar	Trooper	Forli	MV	1,525	M
28 Mar	Torbay	Lillois	MV	3,680	M
7 April	Tuna	U644	UB	749	H
14 April	Taurus	Alcione C.	tanker	520	M
4 June	Truculent	U307	UB	749	H
14 June	Tactician	Rosandra	MV	8,035	M
23 July	Torbay	Aderno	MV	2,610	M
29 July	Trooper	P. Micca	UB	1,545	M
2 Sept	Torbay	Versilia	MV	590	M
16 Oct	Torbay	Kari	MV	1,925	M
10 Nov	Tally-Ho	Kisogawa Maru	tanker	1,914	FE
13 Nov	Taurus	I.34	UB	2,212	FE
22 Nov	Torbay	floating dock		15,000	M**
27 Nov	Torbay	Palma	MV	2,610	M
1944					
11 Jan	Tally-Ho	Kuma	cruiser	5,700	FE
15 Jan	Tally-Ho	Ryuko Maru	MV	2,962	FE
27 Jan	Templar	Kitakami	cruiser	5,500	FE
7 Feb	Taku	Rheinhausen	MV	6,298	H
12 Feb	Taku	H. Fritzen	MV	4,818	H *B
13 Feb	Taku	Bornhofen	MV	3,000	H
15 Feb	Tally-Ho	UIT23	UB	1,448	FE
21 Feb	Tally-Ho	Daigen Maru No. 6	MV	510	FE
24 Mar	Terrapin	Werth	MV	6,256	H
	Terrapin	Schwabenwald	Aux	8,631	H
28 Mar	Truculent	Yasushima Maru	MV	1,910	FE

Date	Submarine	Enemy	Type	Tonnage	Theatre
22 April	Taurus	Gio Hokuan	Aux	558	FE
27 April	Taurus	I.37	UB	2,195	FE *M
3 May	Tantalus	Amagi Maru	MV	3,165	FE
12 May	Trespasser	Kasumi Maru	MV		FE *M
18 May	Tally-Ho	Nichiyoku Maru	MV		FE
*M 28 May	Templar	Tyokai Maru	MV	2,658	FE
10 June	Tantalus	Hyoshi Maru		535	FE
26 June	Truculent	Harukiku Maru		3,040	FE
17 July	Telemachus	I.166	UB	1,575	FE
5 Sept	Tantivy	Shiretoko Maru	MV	1,799	FE
18 Sept	Tradewind	Junyo Maru	MV	5,065	FE
23 Sept	Trenchant	U859	UB	1,126	FE
6 Oct	Tally-Ho	Submarine Chaser	No. 4	100	FE
6 Oct	Zwaardvis	U168	UB	1,126	FE
17 Oct	Zwaardvis	Itsukushima	ML	1,970	FE
2 Nov	Tantalus	Hachijin Maru	MV	1,918	FE
4 Nov	Terrapin	Special Minesweeper	No. 5	615	FE
20 Nov	Tally-Ho	Special Minelayer	No. 4	600	FE
1945					
11 Feb	Tradewind	Nanshin Maru	MV	834	FE
4 Mar	Trenchant Terrapin	Special Submarine Chaser	No. 5	290	FE
12 April	Tapir	U486	UB	749	H
29 April	Tradewind	Takasago Maru	tanker	1,116	FE
25 May	Thorough	Nittei Maru	MV	1,000	FE
25 May	Trenchant	Special Minesweeper	No. 105	215	FE
1 June	Tiptoe	Tobi Maru	MV	982	FE
8 June	Trenchant	Asigara	cruiser	12,700	FE

4. Glossary

AIV: Automatic Inboard Vent. Compensation mechanism for loss of weight when torpedo is fired.

ASDIC: Allied Submarine Detection and Investigation Committee: acronym for submarine detection apparatus.

ASH: Alphabetical designation applying to an aerial, in this case an IFF set. ALF, ANF and APT are similar designations for aerials.

BIBS: Built in Breathing System.

BHP: Brake Horse Power.

Captain S/M: Commanding officer of a submarine flotilla. Usually known by the number of the flotilla he commands: thus Captain S.1 is commanding officer of the 1st Submarine Flotilla.

Casing: Free flooding structure built on to pressure hull.

CO: Commanding Officer.

DA: The amount of 'aim-off' applied during an attack to allow for the target's speed.

DSEA: Davis Submarine Escape apparatus.

DSC: Distinguished Service Cross: a gallantry award for naval officers.

DSM: Distinguished Service Medal: gallantry award for NCOs, common to all three services.

DSO: Distinguished Service Order: gallantry award common to officers of all three services.

EOF: Emergency Oil Fuel.

ERA: Engine Room Artificer. In a submarine the ERA responsible for machinery outside the engine room is known as the 'Outside ERA'.

FOS/M: Flag Officer Submarines.

Hertz (Horn): Protrusion on the upper surface of a contact mine filled with acid which serves as the firing mechanism. When struck by a ship the horn breaks, completing the firing circuit and exploding the mine. Fitted to the Vickers T Mk III mine carried in *Tetrarch*.

HF: High-frequency.

HP: High-pressure (air).

IFF: Identification – Friend/Foe.

Kingstons: Telemotor-operated inlet valves in main and auxiliary tanks.

Kitchen Rudder (effect): Kitchen rudders are a type of shroud around the propeller(s) of small craft which replace the rudder proper. Kitchen Rudder Effect is what happens when an obstruction, such as failed after hydroplanes, interferes with the water flow around the rudder and the boat becomes impossible to steer

LF: Low-frequency.

LP: Low-pressure (air).

OFT: Oil Fuel Tank.

OMEC: One Man Escape Chamber.

OOD: Officer of the Day.

OOW: Officer of the Watch.

Pressure hull: Cylindrical main structure of the submarine.

RA (S): Rear-Admiral (Submarines): professional head of Royal Navy Submarine Service. Also known as Vice-Admiral (S) or Admiral (S) depending on the rank of the flag officer concerned. Title changed to FOS/M in 1948.

Saddle tanks: Ballast tanks external to the pressure hull.

SEBA: Submarine Escape Breathing Apparatus.

Sonar: Sound Navigation and Ranging: post-war acronym of US origin for submarine detection apparatus: replaced ASDIC.

Stopped Trim: State of neutral buoyancy achieved by using the trimming and compensating tanks to balance the boat while the main motors are stopped.

T-Conversion: T-class submarine lengthened and fitted with extra battery for high underwater speed; viz. *Taciturn, Turpin, Totem, Thermopylae, Tiptoe, Trump, Tabard* and *Truncheon*.

T-Streamline: T-class submarine with streamlined casing for enhanced submerged speed, but not lengthened or fitted with additional battery as in the Conversions; viz. *Tireless, Tapir, Talent, Token* and *Teredo*.

TABS: Tower Air Breathing System.

TGM: Torpedo Gunner's Mate.

TI: Torpedo Instructor.

Trim: The fore and aft balance of a submarine when dived. Controlled by the compensating tanks and is the responsibility of the First Lieutenant.

VLF: Very Low Frequency.

WRT: Water Round Torpedo (Tank).

Bibliography

Ackermann, P.   *The Encyclopaedia of HM Submarines, 1901–1955*. Maritime Books, 1989

Admiralty   Naval Staff History: *Submarines* (3 vols.), HMSO, 1953–6

—   Battle Summary No. 29: The attack on the *Tirpitz* by Midget Submarines, 23 September 1943, Operation 'Source'. HMSO, 1948

—   The Development of HM Submarines. BR 3043, MoD Ship Department, 1979

Bagnasco, E.   *Submarines of WW2*. Arms & Armour Press, 1977

Campbell, J.   *Naval Weapons of WW2*. Conway Maritime Press, 1985

Chapman, Paul   *Submarine* Torbay. Robert Hale, London, 1989

Colledge, J. J.   *Ships of the Royal Navy: An Historical Index* (2 vols.), David & Charles, 1969–70

Compton-Hall, Commander P. R.   *The Underwater War, 1939–45.* Blandford Press, 1982

—   *Submarine Warfare: Monsters and Midgets*. Blandford Press, 1985

Cruikshank, G.   *SOE in the Far East*. Oxford University Press, 1983

Evans, A. S.   *Beneath the Waves. A History of HM Submarine Losses 1904–1971*. William Kimber, 1986

Fraccaroli, A.   *Italian Warships of World War II*. Ian Allan, 1968

Friedman, N.   *Submarine Design and Development*. Conway Maritime Press, 1984

—   *Naval Radar*. Conway Maritime Press, 1981

Grove, Eric   *Vanguard to Trident: British Naval Policy since World War II*. USNIP, 1987

Hackmann, W.   *Seek and Strike: Sonar and Anti-Submarine Warfare in the Royal Navy, 1914–1954*. HMSO, 1984

Hezlet, Vice-Admiral Sir A.   *The Submarine and Sea power*. Peter Davies, 1967

—   *The Electron and Sea Power*. Peter Davies, 1975

Hill, D. and Lambert, J.   *The Submarine* Alliance. Conway Maritime Press, 1986

Jones, G.   *Submarines vs. U-boats*. William Kimber, 1986

King, Commander W. D. A.   *Dive and Attack. A Submariner's Story*. William Kimber, 1983

Lipscomb, F. W.   *The British Submarine*. Conway Maritime Press, 1975

Mars, A.   *HMS* Thule *Intercepts*. Elek Books, London, 1956

Rastelli, A.   *Le Navi Del Re*. Sugar Co Se Edizione, 1988

Rauber, V.   *La Marina Italiana Nella Seconda Guerra Mondiale*, vol. XXII, La Lotta Antisommergibile, Ufficio Storico Della Marina Militare, Rome 1978

Roskill, S. W.   *The War at Sea, 1939–45* (3 vols.). HMSO, 1954–61

—   *Naval Policy Between the Wars* (2 vols.). Collins, 1968–76

Shelford, W. O.   *Subsunk!* George Harrap, 1960

Simpson, Rear-Admiral G. W. G.   *Periscope View*. Macmillan, 1972

Stevens, Captain J. S.   *Never Volunteer, A Submariner's Scrapbook*. Solent Printers, 1971

Trenowden, Ian   *The Hunting Submarine. The Fighting Life of HMS* Tally-Ho. William Kimber, 1974

Warren, C. E. T., and Benson, J.   *The Admiralty Regrets*. George Harrap, 1958

—   *Above Us The Waves*. George Harrap, 1953

Winton, J.   *The Forgotten Fleet*. Michael Joseph, 1969

Index